T175 NETWORKED LI
Exploring Information
Communication Technol

Block 4
Health, transport and government
Parts 1–3

Prepared on behalf of the course team
by Allan Jones and Roger Jones

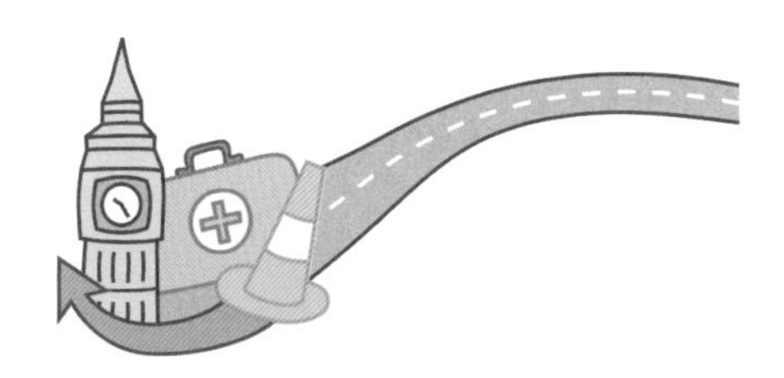

This publication forms part of an Open University course T175 *Networked living*. Details of this and other Open University courses can be obtained from the Student Registration and Enquiry Service, The Open University, PO Box 197, Milton Keynes MK7 6BJ, United Kingdom: tel. +44 (0)870 333 4340, email general-enquiries@open.ac.uk

Alternatively, you may visit the Open University website at http://www.open.ac.uk where you can learn more about the wide range of courses and packs offered at all levels by The Open University.

To purchase a selection of Open University course materials visit http://www.ouw.co.uk, or contact Open University Worldwide, Michael Young Building, Walton Hall, Milton Keynes MK7 6AA, United Kingdom for a brochure. tel. +44 (0)1908 858785; fax +44 (0)1908 858787; e-mail ouwenq@open.ac.uk

The Open University
Walton Hall, Milton Keynes
MK7 6AA

First published 2005. Second edition 2006.

Edited and designed by The Open University.

Typeset in India by Alden Prepress Services, Chennai.

Printed and bound in the United Kingdom by Halstan Printing Group, Amersham.

ISBN 978 0 7492 1522 4

2.1

The paper used in this publication contains pulp sourced from forests independently certified to the Forest Stewardship Council (FSC) principles and criteria. Chain of custody certification allows the pulp from these forests to be tracked to the end use (see www.fsc-uk.org).

Course Team List

Karen Kear, course team chair

Ernie Taylor, course manager

Patricia Telford, course secretary

Academic staff

Mustafa Ali

Chris Bissell

David Chapman

Geoff Einon

Clem Herman

Allan Jones

Roger Jones

John Monk

Nicky Moss

Elaine Thomas

Mirabelle Walker

Judith Williams

John Woodthorpe

Media production staff

Geoff Austin

Deirdre Bethune

Annette Booz

Sophia Braybrooke

Sarah Crompton

Jamie Daniels

Vicky Eves

Alison George

Mark Kesby

Lynn Short

External assessor

Prof. Philip Witting, University of Glamorgan

Contents

Part 2 Road transport

Part 3 E-government

Part 1
Health

Roger Jones

1 Introduction

Health is of fundamental importance to us all because it sets a baseline for the quality of our lives. I expect you already have a fair idea about what health means to you, but you may like to know that the World Health Organization (WHO) has defined health in the following way:

> Health is a state of complete physical, mental and social well-being and not merely the absence of disease or infirmity.
>
> World Health Organization (1946)

This definition of health has remained unchanged since 1946. It's interesting that it includes the social condition. The idea of the support of society, or at a more local level a community, is an important aspect of healthcare.

In this part of Block 4 I shall not, however, be looking at health itself, but rather at how ICTs are influencing, and even changing, some aspects of healthcare. I shall be focusing on *information* about health, and on how ICTs support the *communication* of that information.

In Section 2 I look at how information about health can be communicated to people. You will see that familiar ICT systems such as the internet, telephones and broadcast TV and radio are all being used to this end. But simply making information available is not enough: people need to be able to access the information provided, and they need to be able to use it appropriately. Therefore in Section 2, as well as looking at how ICT systems can be used to communicate health information, I will discuss the issues of who has access to the information and how the information is used.

In Section 3 I look at a different aspect of communicating information about health: how ICT systems can be used to communicate information about the health of a patient to a medical professional so that treatment can be provided at a distance. Telemedicine is the name given to this new and still-developing field of treatment at a distance. Telemedicine can even include surgery at a distance (telesurgery), where it's crucial that the surgeon gets information back quickly about his or her actions. Telemedicine can therefore make strong demands on ICT systems.

At present in the UK and elsewhere, much information about patients is held on paper and in a variety of locations. In the UK an ambitious project is under way which will computerise these records so that the information can be communicated quickly to medical professionals whenever they need it and wherever they are. Access is again an issue, but in a different way from in Section 2, as here an important aspect of the system is to restrict access to authorised personnel. This project, which includes much more than just computerising records – for

example, an online booking system for hospital appointments and an online service for transmitting prescriptions – makes considerable demands on ICTs. The project and related ICTs are the topic of the final section, Section 4.

Although some of my focus in this material is on what is happening in the UK, I shall also be looking more widely. Health is of global importance. You can see this in the United Nations Millennium Declaration, made in 2000, which committed its 191 member states to achieve a set of eight goals (see box) by 2015. No fewer than three of these goals (numbers 4 to 6) relate explicitly to health, and another one does so implicitly (number 1). Further, a target under the eighth goal is 'In cooperation with the private sector, make available the benefits of new technologies – especially information and communications technologies'. So the use of ICT systems in the context of health is an important example and one which has potential benefit for everyone.

The eight goals set out in the United Nations Millennium Declaration

1. Eradicate extreme poverty and hunger
2. Achieve universal primary education
3. Promote gender equality and empower women
4. Reduce child mortality
5. Improve maternal health
6. Combat HIV/AIDS, malaria and other diseases
7. Ensure environmental sustainability
8. Develop a global partnership for development

United Nations (2000)

2 Accessing health information

You will need the following resources while studying this section:

- *your computer for Activity 4 (in Section 2.2);*
- *your computer with internet access for Activity 3 (in Section 2.2) and during your study of Section 2.5;*
- *your computer and the T175 DVD during your study of Section 2.7.*

2.1 Access

Reliable information about health and healthcare can make a big difference in people's lives, and ICT systems have a significant role to play in communicating this type of information. But people do need to be able to access the information that is available, and so access is my first topic in Section 2.

I'll start with the industrialised, developed areas of the world, where ICT systems are increasingly being employed to support health provision. In the United Kingdom, for example, the National Health Service (NHS) provides a service called NHS Direct, which offers several alternatives to visiting a doctor (at least in the first instance). At the time of writing NHS Direct can be accessed using three different sorts of ICT system: by means of a telephone, an interactive digital television channel and a set of web pages.

Most people in the UK have access to a telephone, but access to digital television and access to the internet are less widespread. You might like to think for a moment about some of your acquaintances who do not have access to the internet in their home, and the reasons for this. Maybe it's because of the costs involved, or a lack of computer skills, or even a lack of availability of a suitable access point (as in, for example, a bedsit)? Cost, skill and availability are three important factors in access to all ICT systems and consequently to the health information that they can carry. Unfortunately, those who are less skilled and less well off have fewer opportunities to use modern ICT systems to help improve their health.

If that is true in the industrialised nations, it is even more so in the less developed parts of the world, as you will see in the following activity.

Activity 1 (exploratory)

The article 'Behind the digital divide' (*The Economist*, 2005) in the appendix is not focused on health issues, but it contains much that is relevant to the idea of using ICT systems to support health information in one particular country: India.

(a) Turn to this article and read it through once quickly to get an overview of its content. What ICT systems does it mention and what health-related benefits does it claim for them? (Note that the article uses the term 'ICTs' in a more limited sense than does T175; I'd like you to work with T175's use of the term here as introduced earlier in the course.)

(b) Now read the article more slowly and answer the following questions:

(i) Earlier I mentioned cost, skill and availability as important access issues for ICT systems in industrialised nations. From your reading of this article, do the same issues apply to India, an example of a developing country?

(ii) From your reading of the article, which seems to you a more effective way of communicating health information to poor people in rural India: the internet or broadcast radio?

Comment

(a) The ICT systems mentioned are: computers with an internet link (using a wireless connection); telephones; broadcast television; a satellite-based system to track fish; broadcast radio.

The system that comprises computers with internet links is said to provide 'health advice', and the 'details of government welfare schemes' mentioned may include those that are health-related. This system is also said to have improved the social well-being of women, which fits with the wider sense of 'health' in the WHO definition. No health-related benefits are claimed for the other ICT systems mentioned.

(b)

(i) According to the article, cost and skill both apply (Arumugam and Thillan are trying to survive on a few pence a day; both they and Thuradi are illiterate). In fact, cost seems to be the key factor: Ashok Jhunjhunwala describes it as a 'deciding factor'.

As the article is focused on making ICTs available through the new 'Knowledge Centres', it is hardly surprising that availability – or, rather, lack of it – is not an issue that figures in the article. But it is easy to imagine that in small towns and villages without such centres availability is also an issue.

(ii) The article leads me to believe that at the moment broadcast radio is more effective than the internet. Do you agree?

From your work in Activity 1, you will have seen that in developing countries access is a major issue in the communication of all kinds of information, including health-related information, via ICT systems.

At present more 'traditional' systems such as broadcast radio may be more effective than newer technologies for many citizens of such countries.

In Sections 2.2 to 2.5 I am going to discuss four types of ICT system and their use in communicating health information: telephones; broadcast radio; digital television; the internet. In all four cases I shall illustrate how the ICT system is being used to communicate health information, and I shall also discuss access issues for the ICT system. In addition, for all systems except the internet, I shall introduce some relevant features of the technology of the ICT system.

So in Section 2.2 I'll be discussing the telephone, starting with an example of how it can be used to access health information in the UK.

2.2 Telephones

An example of health information by phone

I mentioned in Section 2.1 that the UK's NHS Direct scheme is made available in three ways, one of which is via the telephone. I'll describe an experience I had with this telephone service in 2005, to give you an idea of what it was offering at that time.

When writing the material for this block, I experienced persistent discomfort and sometimes pain along the whole length of one arm. I suspected the problem was Repetitive Strain Injury (RSI) caused by frequent use of my computer keyboard and mouse, though I couldn't be sure as I had no previous experience of this complaint.

During my first call to NHS Direct, initial details were taken and I was placed in a (non-urgent) queue to have my call returned. After approximately 10 minutes I was telephoned and some further details were taken including those of my own doctor.

When I explained about the nature of my concern, the nurse enquired about things which I hadn't thought about. For instance, whether the pain was stationary or had moved its location. This could be significant.

Having followed a fairly extensive question-and-answer dialogue, the nurse confirmed that the problem was likely to be RSI. The nurse then informed me of similar problems experienced by staff at NHS Direct call centres. (Nurses at these centres make intensive use of computers during phone calls.) Several remedies were suggested, based upon the experiences at NHS Direct.

Although RSI can be a serious problem, in my case this consultation helped reassure me. It also told me the type of measures that I could take to reduce its impact. My consultation was completed within half an hour of my query and I found the experience satisfactory on this occasion.

You'll see from this description that the telephone is being used interactively in NHS Direct: there is an exchange of information. It is possible to envisage an alternative way of setting up this phone service, whereby people phone one of a range of phone numbers, depending on the problem they are experiencing or the type of query they have, and then select from a menu of choices ('Press 1 if you ...'). But most people dislike this sort of menu-driven service and listening to recorded messages; they much prefer 'talking to a real person' on the phone. So, as in the case of NHS Direct, a telephone information service about health is most effective if it can be used interactively.

Technology

In the UK, as in most developed countries, just about everyone has access to a telephone, and we take it for granted that we can use it to seek help. But to be able to use a telephone we must be within reach of some form of telephone network. Such networks developed gradually over many years in the industrialised world and became infrastructure networks which still provide the support to many of the newer communication technologies that have since been developed.

I'll briefly remind you of some of the details of the infrastructure of telephone networks. These networks provide connections in a hierarchical manner. At the lowest level is each connection from an individual home or business to the local switching centre (switching centres are informally known as telephone exchanges). This connection is sometimes known as the 'local loop' and is made by a simple pair of twisted wires. Users of a cable telephone have a coaxial cable link to a shared fibre-optic cable instead. At the next level up are the interconnections between switching centres, where high-capacity fibre-optic cables carry the digital data associated with large numbers of telephone calls (or data streams) nationally. At the highest level are connections between international switching centres in different countries. These may also be by fibre-optic cable, or they may be via satellite. The term public switched telephone network (PSTN) is used to refer to a national communication infrastructure network.

In mobile telephone systems the wired local loop is replaced by radio signals between a user's handset and a base station. Because the geographical area served by a base station is known as a cell, mobile telephony is sometimes called 'cellular telephony'. Base stations are connected, either by radio or by cables, to mobile switching centres. Mobile switching centres are, in turn, connected by cables to switching centres in the PSTN, so that calls can be made between 'fixed' and mobile phones.

In a developed country the wires and cables of the infrastructure for 'fixed' telephones will have been built up over several decades and will now serve the whole country. In developing countries such an infrastructure may be much less developed at some levels and in some

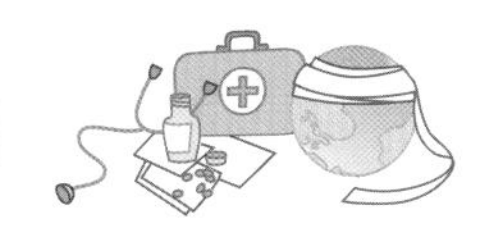

geographical areas. In these countries it can make better economic sense to adopt cellular wireless technology at the local level. This can be done in one of two ways. First, it can be done in exactly the same way as in developed countries: a mobile telephone network can be set up. In Kenya, for example, the number of mobile phone subscribers is already over ten times the number of subscribers to the country's rather limited 'fixed' phone system (England, 2005). Second, a wireless link can be provided from a local switching centre to people's homes, or to public phone kiosks, which avoids the expense of installing wired local loops.

Activity 2 (exploratory)

The use of a wireless link to people's homes is a use of cellular wireless technology. Why do you think cells would be used in this case?

Comment

You should recall that wireless signals decrease in strength with distance from a base station. So one reason for using cells is to ensure that every home in a geographical area has a signal of adequate strength.

There is another reason, which you may perhaps be aware of: dividing a particular geographical area down into small cells increases capacity. This is because there are practical limits to how many phones in a cell can simultaneously use a wireless phone service. More cells means more users. So if the homes using the cellular service are relatively densely packed, many small cells will be needed to provide the needed capacity.

Access to telephones

In Activity 3 I'm going to ask you to go online to download some recent statistical information regarding telephone access in various parts of the world. This information is made available through the United Nations Statistical Division. One of the main functions of this division of the UN is to collect, process and disseminate statistical information. Some of this information is used to indicate whether and when the millennium goals I referred to at the end of Section 1 are achieved.

Then in Activity 4, where you can work offline, I shall ask you to use a spreadsheet to compare access in four countries.

The statistics you will be collecting and using in this pair of activities are available from the same website that gives the millennium goals themselves. Through this website data is available for specific indicators for each target listed under the millennium goals. The target of interest here is the one relating to ICTs that I mentioned earlier: '[...] make

available the benefits of new technologies – especially information and communications technologies'. One of the indicators given for this is:

Telephone lines and cellular subscribers per 100 population

and this pair of activities relates to this indicator.

First, however, a word of caution: the number of phone *users* may be considerably higher than the sum of the number of telephone lines and cellular subscribers. This is because shared use is likely. In the home all members of a family are likely to share a single line, and as you'll see shortly, in developing countries there are mobile phone subscribers who make their living by offering their phone as a public payphone.

Activity 3 (exploratory)

Go to the 'Resources' area on the T175 course website (use the Resources tab at the top). In the Block 4 Resources section, follow the link 'UN data on telephone lines and cellular subscribers'.

You will be presented with a table giving data on telephone access for almost 200 countries. To reduce the amount of data displayed, select '10 recent years' from the drop-down 'Years' list at the top of the table. You will probably find there is no data available for the current year, and there may also be none for the previous year (depending upon the month when you carry out this activity).

The site offers you the facility to download this table into a spreadsheet file. This will mean that you can work on the data offline. Click on the 'download results' option at the top of the table. From the window that opens choose 'Save', then select an appropriate location for the file from the 'Save As' window. You can keep the default file name 'Results' or choose your own (e.g. Health Activity 3 Results). Note that the file type will probably be set to Microsoft Excel Comma Separated Values (csv) file. Don't worry about this, even if you do not use Microsoft Excel. Make a note of the file name and remember where you have stored this file: you will need it in the next activity.

You may now terminate your internet connection if you wish.

Comment

The file will be saved in the csv format. This format is used to transfer data between spreadsheets from different software products. (This is similar to the way the rtf format allows data to be transferred between word-processor programs from different software companies.) A csv file is a text file that separates every item of data by a comma. If you were to open the csv file just saved using a text editor (such as Notepad, which can be found in Windows Accessories) you would see something similar to Figure 1.

```
Results.csv - Notepad
File Edit Format Help
"Millennium Indicator: 'Telephone lines and cellular subscribers per 100 population (ITU
estimates)'"
"Data last updated on 10 Mar 2005"

Country,1996,1997,1998,1999,2000,2001,2002,2003,2004,2005,
"Afghanistan",          0.14,          0.13,          0.14,          0.13,
  0.13,          0.13,          0.25,          1.18, , ,
"Albania",          2.12,          2.89,          3.90,          4.88,
5.90,          19.12,          34.77,          44.10, , ,
"Algeria",          4.52,          4.88,          5.07,          5.58,
6.08,          6.42,          7.38,          11.46, , ,
"American Samoa",          28.41,          29.22,          29.36,          29.01, , ,
, , , ,
"Andorra",          51.34,          54.77,          62.75,          72.17,
74.05,          89.93,          93.11,          115.15, , ,
"Angola",          0.50,          0.60,          0.62,          0.73,
0.73,          1.23,          1.54, , , ,
"Anguilla",          59.69,          76.61,          78.75,          89.12,
100.62,          68.98, , , , ,
"Antigua and Barbuda",          42.70,          45.88,          48.86,          60.24,
        78.63,          80.42,          97.76, , , ,
"Argentina",          19.76,          24.30,          28.06,          33.23,
38.90,          41.64,          39.64, , , ,
"Armenia",          15.34,          15.11,          14.86,          14.52,
14.49,          14.65,          16.17,          17.84, , ,
"Aruba",          42.57,          40.44,          43.03,          49.41,
51.79,          85.03, , , , ,
"Australia",          71.87,          75.72,          77.19,          84.89,
98.72,          111.50,          119.42,          126.18, , ,
"Austria",          56.54,          64.37,          78.85,          101.51,
126.22,          131.21,          131.86,          135.95, , ,
"Azerbaijan",          8.74,          9.15,          9.72,          14.29,
 15.58,          19.96,          22.03,          24.25, , ,
"Bahamas",          33.25,          36.08,          38.49,          42.18,
47.84,          59.89,          79.59,          78.19, , ,
"Bahrain",          32.09,          35.78,          41.33,          48.26,
59.35,          72.96,          83.99,          90.60, , ,
```

Figure 1 A csv file viewed using Notepad

The file you downloaded and saved in Activity 3 holds data for some 200 countries. In the next activity you will be looking in more detail at a subset of this data. You will do this by creating a chart.

I shall ask you to look only at the data for the countries Bangladesh, China (mainland China, not the special administrative regions such as Hong Kong), Denmark and Uganda. I have chosen these four very different countries to provide a 'snapshot' of different regions of the world. Bangladesh is a high-population Asian country where poverty is a serious problem. China, at the time of writing, is developing rapidly, and Denmark is fairly typical of a mature (in development terms) European nation. I took Uganda as an example of sub-Saharan Africa (an African country situated south of the Sahara desert).

Activity 4 (exploratory)

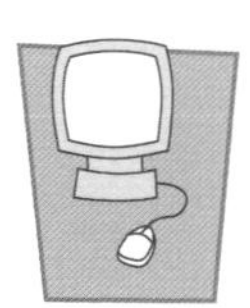

Open your spreadsheet program, and then use Open from the File menu to open the spreadsheet you saved during Activity 3. In order to open a csv file you may have to change the file type to 'All files' in the dialogue box that opens when you choose Open.

Identify the rows for the countries Bangladesh, China (mainland China), Denmark and Uganda.

Now find the most recent year for which data is available for all four countries. You will then be able to select the data for the five most recent consecutive years for which the data-set is complete.

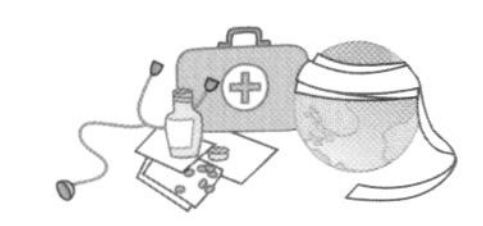

In your spreadsheet, delete the rows that give data for all countries other than the four chosen, and delete the columns that give data for years other than the most recent five for which data is available. To do this, highlight the rows or columns to be deleted and choose Delete Cells (StarOffice) or Delete (Excel) from the Edit menu. (To highlight an entire row or column, click on the row or column header. To highlight a group of rows or columns, click on the row or column header at the beginning of the group and drag across the header to highlight the whole group.)

As well as the title rows, you should now be left with six columns and five rows of data.

Create a chart to display the data for each year along the horizontal axis using a similar method to activities you have carried out with charts earlier in the course. However, in this case, because the dates are ordered in rows rather than in columns, you will need to select the 'Rows' option when choosing the data series. Add a suitable chart title and axis labels.

When you have completed your chart look at it critically, first using a linear axis and then a logarithmic axis. You will probably need to set the crossing point on the logarithmic scale at 0.1 in order to present the data without negative values appearing on the vertical axis. To do this you will need to make an adjustment in the scale settings for the vertical axis (double-click on the vertical axis to access these settings). In StarOffice, untick the 'Automatic' box and enter 0.1. If you are using Excel, enter 0.1 in the 'Crosses at' box.

Examine your graph. How is telephone availability changing from year to year? How might this affect attempts to improve levels of health information in the more remote regions of developing countries? Write a few notes that answer these questions.

Comment

My chart is shown in Figure 2, and my notes are as follows.

From my chart, I noticed a big difference in the availability of telephone lines and cellular subscribers in Bangladesh and Uganda compared with Denmark. China lay between these extremes. Using a linear vertical scale the columns for Bangladesh or Uganda were almost indistinguishable from zero.

Using a logarithmic vertical axis it was easier to compare the trends in the four countries, but it was more difficult to read off the absolute values.

Although the values for Denmark were high (from about 120 to 160 telephone lines and cellular subscribers per 100 population), I could detect a levelling off in the most recent years – the increase from year

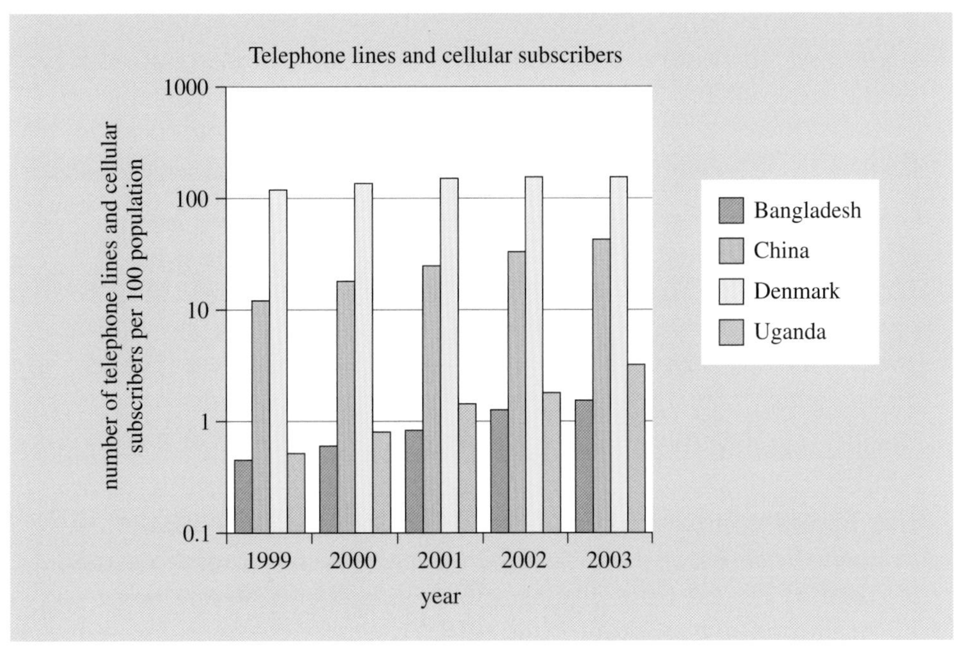

Figure 2 Chart showing telephone availability in selected countries on a logarithmic scale

to year was reducing. This compared with a much stronger year-to-year increase for China, but China's growth was from a lower starting point.

When I thought about the data for the four countries, I wondered how many of the telephone lines are actually to people's homes, because I suspect that many telephone lines would be to businesses and government establishments. So there is probably even less availability to poor people than these figures suggest, especially in rural areas in countries such as Bangladesh and Uganda. Also, those who are not employed will not have access to telephones through their workplace.

On the other hand, an article about ICTs in developing countries drew my attention to the extent to which phones are shared in Bangladesh (see the box 'Grameen Telecom: offering telephone access to Bangladeshis'), so it is important to remember that data about numbers of telephone lines and cellular subscribers may well underestimate the availability of phones in developing countries.

Nevertheless, the data about access to telephones in developing countries such as Bangladesh and Uganda shows just what a challenge it is for even a relatively traditional ICT such as the telephone to be used to communicate health information to individuals. A telephone service such as the one offered by the UK's NHS Direct would be truly accessible to only a small proportion of the population. This is less so in China; the figures indicate that if growth continues at the same rate then in a few years there will be

100 telephone lines and cellular subscribers per 100 population, suggesting that a service like NHS Direct could then be relatively widely accessible.

Grameen Telecom: offering telephone access to Bangladeshis

Grameen Telecom grew out of Grameen Bank, which has been offering 'microloans' (loans for very small amounts) for some 30 years to poor Bangladeshis in order to help them to set up a small business. Grameen Telecom is a franchising enterprise which offers microloans to franchisees to enable them to buy a mobile phone, which they then operate as a payphone for their neighbours, thus enabling them to pay back their loan and make a living.

This franchise enterprise has been very successful. In 2005, Grameen Technology had '95 000 franchisees, covering more than 50 000 of the 68 000 villages in Bangladesh and serving some 60 million people' (Brewer et al., 2005).

In spite of increasing access to telephones, radio may offer a better opportunity of communicating health-related information to people in developing countries such as Bangladesh and Uganda, and it is this ICT system that I shall consider next.

2.3 Broadcast radio

Health information by broadcast radio

Just how important is radio for disseminating information that assists healthy living? The term 'to broadcast' means to send the same message simultaneously to all users on a network, and this hints at the power of radio. I'll start by asking you to assess the use of broadcast radio for health information in your own country.

Activity 5 (exploratory)

Think of examples of radio programmes you have listened to recently which have included health-related information. Jot down some examples of the programmes and the issues covered, then compare your findings with mine.

Comment

I live in the UK, so my list is based on the radio programmes here. These are the ones that I can remember having health-related issues:

- BBC Radio 2, 'The Jeremy Vine Show' and its predecessor – frequent topical health features and visiting doctor to take listeners' questions.
- Most stations – news reports on health items, some bringing good news (breakthroughs in treatments), others bad (potential of skin damage from sun or 'sun-beds').
- BBC Radio 4 – various programmes on science and medicine with examples of advances in medicines, research news, new treatments and surgical procedures.

The last activity will probably have reminded you that plenty of health-related information is communicated using conventional radio services in your own country. In fact broadcast radio is an important means for delivering health-related information to people in most parts of the world.

Access and technology

When the seriousness of HIV/AIDS became apparent, experts in the World Health Organization believed that education was vital in combating the spread of the AIDS virus in Africa, because there was no cure. Radio broadcasting offered one way of informing and advising many people about the risks.

Although the message did reach many of those at risk, many others, especially those in rural areas, did not have access to a radio receiver. In many cases this was because they did not have access to mains electricity, and for those living at a subsistence level batteries can be prohibitively expensive. The wind-up radio (see Figure 3) provided a solution to this and has become a famous example of innovative problem solving. This radio, also known as the clockwork radio, was invented by Trevor Baylis in 1992. Winding up a spring stores sufficient

Figure 3 An example of a wind-up radio

energy to power the radio for a period of about one hour. The invention gave many people in Africa access to reliable health-related information for the first time.

The project was initially financed by Liberty Life, a South African insurance company. Aid agencies such as the United Nations High Commissioner for Refugees and the International Red Cross then became active in distributing the radios to those in need.

Avoiding the need for mains electricity or batteries

Many people in rural areas do not have access to mains electricity. For example, only 20% of the continent of Africa has access to electricity (Balancing Act, 2005). Electricity is required for all ICT devices and much medical instrumentation. Having no electricity supply could restrict the work of medical professionals in the field and limit the facilities available to patients.

You might suppose that, as far as ICT devices are concerned, portable devices such as notebook computers, personal digital assistants, mobile telephones and so on could overcome the problem. However, if there is no access to electricity then how can their batteries be recharged?

In fact, the experience gained from the wind-up radio has led to a wind-up charger being developed for use with specific mobile telephone handsets, to provide power for making calls and recharging batteries. Similar devices with increased output power are being developed as I write – for use with portable computers as well as some types of medical equipment. One design uses a foot-operated wind-up mechanism to generate the power needed (Balancing Act, 2005).

Although the wind-up radio has helped the problem of radio use in areas without mains electricity, there remains the problem of coverage. By 'coverage' I mean a sufficiently strong broadcast signal being available over a wide geographical area. There are two ways of providing such a signal; one is by terrestrial broadcasting and the other by satellite broadcasting.

Although my focus in this section is broadcast radio, most of what is said about terrestrial and satellite broadcasts is equally applicable to broadcast television.

Terrestrial radio signals are transmitted using particular radio frequencies from aerials mounted on tall masts. These masts need to be sited so that sufficient signal strength can be received over the whole reception area.

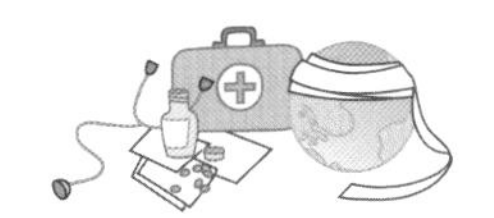

In practice signal strength diminishes rapidly with distance from the transmitting aerial, a phenomenon known as attenuation. In addition, any obstructions in the line of sight – such as buildings, hills and the curvature of the Earth – can further degrade the received signals and cause poor reception.

Satellite technology can provide the means to beam sufficient radio stations to cater for different languages and cultures to most of the world's populated areas. But although satellites can provide cover over large areas, they are expensive to launch and maintain.

Satellites transmit at frequencies within the microwave portion of the electromagnetic spectrum. The frequencies are chosen so that the signals can penetrate the Earth's atmosphere without large losses in signal strength. A satellite will be equipped with at least one antenna, which is usually dish-shaped (a 'dish'). As the distances from transmitter to receiver are large, signals received from satellites are usually quite weak and the receiving radio set needs a larger aerial than is the case with terrestrial broadcasts – again, a dish is normally used.

The coverage provided by a satellite depends on its height above the Earth's surface, as you can see in the two-dimensional representations in Figure 4. (For clarity, I have exaggerated the satellite's size in Figure 4.) The further away the satellite is, the larger the geographical area it serves, as shown in Figures 4(a) and (b). Sometimes the term 'footprint' is used for the area on the Earth's surface covered by a satellite's beam. You can therefore think of Figure 4 as showing satellite footprints for two different satellite heights.

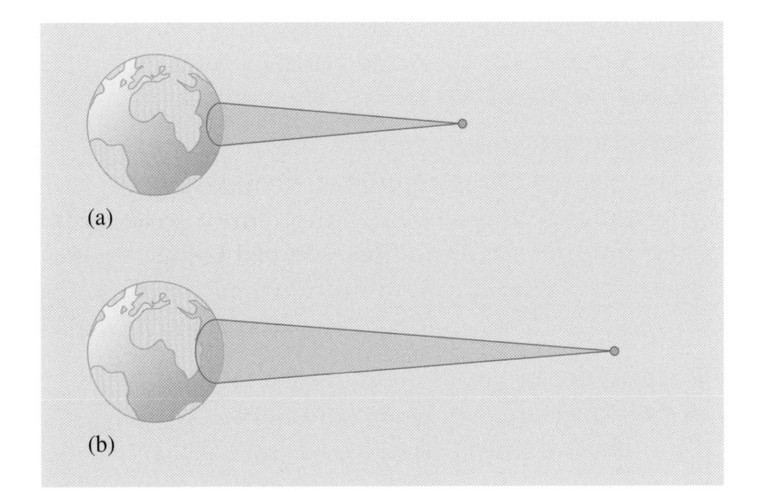

Figure 4 The area covered depends on the satellite's height above the Earth's surface: (a) the satellite is closer and the area covered is smaller; (b) the satellite is further away and the area covered is larger

The footprint does not depend only upon the height of the satellite, however; it also depends on the width of the signal beam. By 'width' I mean the angle of the beam: a beam with a small angle is narrow in

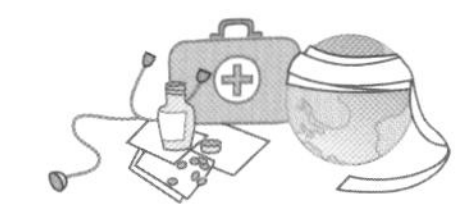

width while a beam with a larger angle is broader in width. In Figure 4 the beam width was a fixed value, but the width can be changed. For a fixed height of satellite a greater beam width produces a larger footprint, as in Figures 5(a) and (b). But there is a maximum beam width beyond which increasing the beam width will have no effect, as shown in Figure 5(c).

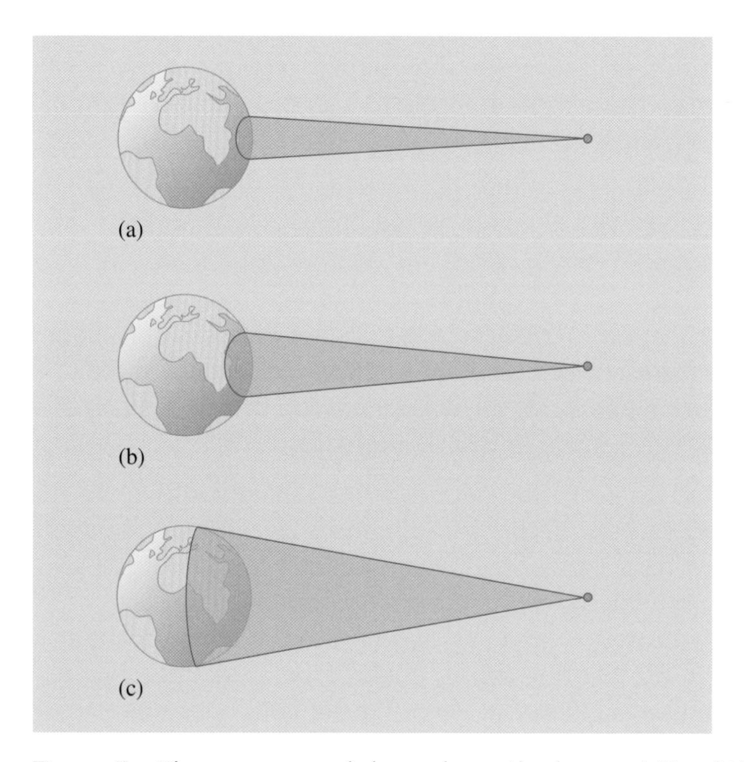

Figure 5 The area covered depends on the beam width of the satellite's signal: (a) the beam width is smallest and the coverage is also smallest; (b) the larger beam width produces a larger footprint; (c) shows the maximum coverage achievable – increasing the beam width will not increase the footprint

In some cases, the beam transmitted is also carefully directed towards a chosen set of countries. You can see this in Figure 6 in the box about Worldspace, a relatively new digital radio satellite broadcasting service. This service uses three angled beams per satellite rather than just a single beam.

Worldspace

Worldspace provides subscription-based digital radio satellite broadcasting services over large areas of three continents. You may like to have a look at the website (http://www.worldspace.com) next time you are online.

When I looked at the Worldspace site in June 2005, the coverage was as shown in Figure 6. Three satellites, Afristar™, Asiastar™ and the planned Ameristar™, provide services to the corresponding continents of Africa, Asia and (South) America. Additional services are likely to be added.

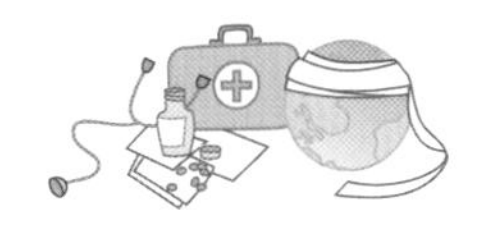

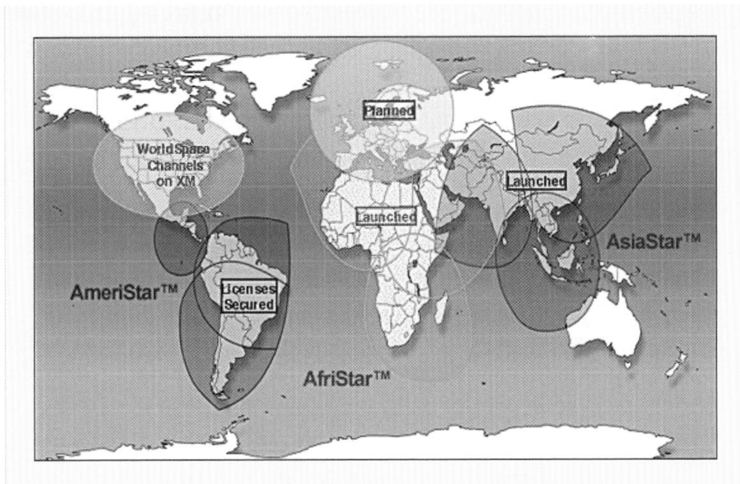

Figure 6 The coverage provided by Worldspace's satellites

An examination of the range of programmes on offer revealed that many were 'imported', for example from American- or British-based broadcasting services; but that other services were 'home-based' with opportunities to include local issues, such as those on health, nutrition, and disease prevention in a form to suit local culture and language.

Figure 7 shows a Worldspace receiver which includes a small receiving antenna. This particular example requires three C-type battery cells or alternatively power from an AC mains adaptor, so the supply of power could still be a restriction to use, and price a restriction to ownership (quite apart from the cost of subscribing to the service). However, community rather than individual ownership could alleviate these constraints.

Figure 7 A radio for use with Worldspace

You have seen that the choice of satellite height and beam width affects the footprint of the satellite. By suitable choice of these parameters, satellites can be made to broadcast radio signals to selected areas of the world, transmitting a variety of programmes to the various countries within the covered area as required.

Geostationary satellites – that is, those whose orbit is chosen such that they remain 'fixed' above a certain point above the Earth's equator – must orbit at a particular height, so it is their beam width that must be appropriately chosen to give a required coverage. But in the case of so-called low earth orbit (LEO) satellites, both height and beam width can be varied.

It's easy to use a scale diagram to find the beam width needed for the maximum footprint on the Earth's surface for a geostationary satellite, as in Figure 8. This can be a useful alternative to doing a calculation. The radius of the Earth is approximately 6.4×10^6 m and the height of a geostationary satellite is approximately 36×10^6 m. I have simply drawn these as 6.4 units and 36 units in Figure 8. Because the diagram is to scale a protractor can be used to measure the beam width. The angle is approximately 17°. A smaller angle than this would give a more restricted coverage, and there would be no point in making the angle larger.

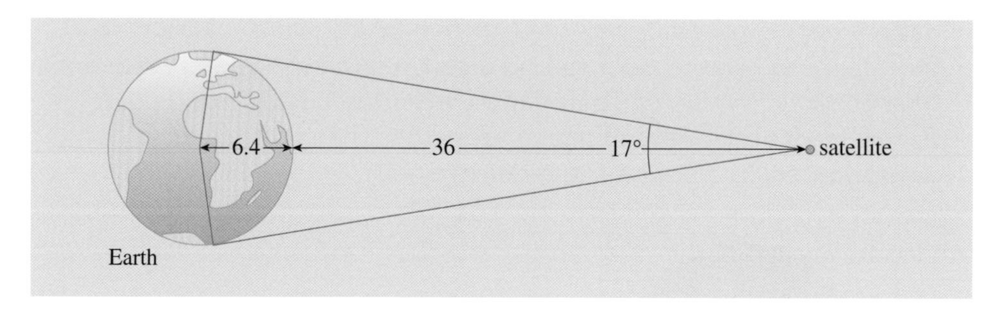

Figure 8 This scale diagram shows that the beam width which gives maximum coverage for a geostationary satellite is 17°

You can see from Figure 8 that the footprint of the beam from a geostationary satellite cannot include regions in the far north or the far south of the earth. Fortunately, few people live in the world's coldest regions.

Three geostationary satellites in orbit above the equator could in principle provide cover to the majority of the Earth's population. Each satellite, would, however, need to transmit many different programmes to the group of countries within its footprint and so the bandwidth available could well become a limiting factor. One way of overcoming this limitation is to use more than three satellites. Another way is to use more than one beam per satellite, limiting the beam width and angling the beams, as in the Worldspace satellites. Different groups of programmes can then be transmitted in each beam.

Activity 6 (exploratory)

Look back to Figure 6, which shows the coverage of the Worldspace satellites. Do you think Worldspace's satellites are geostationary? Why?

Comment

Perhaps this is a bit of a trick question, because only geostationary satellites can have fixed footprints! (LEO satellites move across the sky and so their footprint on the Earth moves too.) So Worldspace's satellites must be geostationary.

2.4 Digital television

Access

I have emphasised how important radio broadcasting is in reaching a large number of people who may otherwise have very limited access to health information. Television can also have an important role to play. This is particularly so in the more developed world, where access to TV is more widespread. Digital television broadcasting is, however, set to replace analogue television broadcasting in many countries, and I have chosen to focus on digital television here because it offers increased options for accessing health information. This is because it can provide more channels, and also include static display screens with which the user can interact via their remote controller.

In reading the material in this section, do bear in mind that for much of the world's population the sorts of services and technology described are totally inaccessible on cost and availability grounds.

An example of health information via digital TV

In Section 2.2 I introduced the UK's NHS Direct telephone service. NHS Direct is available by other means as well, and in this section I shall focus on NHS Direct Interactive, which uses digital TV and was first introduced, as a satellite broadcast service, in December 2004. At its inception it offered about 3000 screens of basic health information, along with a health encyclopedia, general advice on health matters such as diet and nutrition, and video clips covering a wide range of health topics. Information on NHS services such as directories of doctors, dentists, pharmacies and hospitals was also available. Information was mostly in the form of text, with some accompanying images. Sixteen different languages were provided to suit a diverse range of ethnic backgrounds.

Figure 9 shows the style of an introductory screen in this early service. You can see that the screen includes a menu, and this is the visible part of a menu system which includes various levels of sub-menu. Using the digital television remote control unit, a viewer could find and select the required information.

Figure 9 Screen of an early version of NHS Direct Interactive

NHS Direct Interactive is expected to develop a range of transactional services, allowing the booking of surgery appointments and the ordering of repeat prescriptions. NHS Direct Interactive is likely to become available on all forms of digital television in the UK: satellite, cable and terrestrial.

Digital TV includes interactive features, but what exactly is meant by this? Full interactivity is a two-way process. A telephone conversation, for instance, relies upon two directions of communication. In broadcast technologies, though, communication is conventionally from the broadcaster to the user: just one direction. Therefore a return path is required if messages are to be sent from the user to the broadcaster.

So what happens if you are viewing digital television and are invited to make some response via your remote controller? For example, you might be looking at a static display screen on NHS Direct Interactive and wish to make a menu choice. Something changes if you press a button, but in what sense are you interacting? The answer is that you are not interacting with the broadcaster, but with your set-top box. This set-top box receives the broadcast streams from which you are able to make some selection of content.

To gauge the level of interactivity possible with a digital television service think about the situation where, during a television programme,

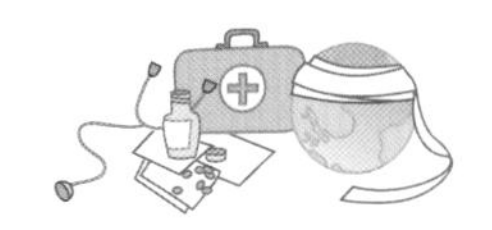

viewers are asked to indicate some preference by casting a vote. Here the message needs to go back to the broadcaster, not just to the set-top box. In such cases, viewers are invited to dial a particular telephone number, or perhaps send a text message or email. The return path to the broadcaster is very different from the path the broadcast took to the viewer. (Even in the case of a cable TV viewer using a cable phone, there will come a point where the phone call will be routed through the PSTN, and this differs from the route taken by the broadcast to the home.) Although expressing a preference may be called interactivity, it is very far from the level of interactivity provided by a phone conversation, for instance.

Activity 7 (exploratory)

Which of the services planned for NHS Direct Interactive that I have mentioned would require a return path between the service user and broadcaster, and why?

Comment

I mentioned two services of this type: booking appointments (for example, with a surgery or clinic) and ordering repeat prescriptions.

To book an appointment you would need to know the available time slots. You would then need to signal your choice of appointment back to NHS Direct Interactive through a return path. This would allow your chosen time slot to be registered.

Similarly, to use NHS Direct Interactive for ordering repeat prescriptions you would send information about yourself (your identity and what medication you were ordering) using a return path.

I hope you are now in a position to think carefully about what is meant when a service is described as 'interactive' and are able to distinguish between the full, two-way interactivity that, say, telephones provide and the quasi-interactivity of, for example, some services offered by digital TV.

Technology

I have indicated that digital TV can offer more channels than analogue, and also provide additional information of various types – static displays of information, for example, or user choice of camera or camera angles at a sports event. The intriguing feature of digital TV is that a great number of such digital channels can be packed into the same broadcasting band as was used for just a few analogue ones. In this subsection I shall explore how this can be achieved.

Two major factors are at work. One is the use of compression techniques similar to those presented earlier in the course. Pictures, speech, music and other audio components are all compressed before transmission, and then decompressed in the set-top box or integrated digital receiver.

The other factor is more subtle: the transmission capacity is used flexibly. Consider, for example, some typical television images. Some may be relatively static (for example, a stationary figure debating some issue in a current affairs programme) while others may be fast-moving (a chase in an action movie). These different types of image will require different data rates to support them (low for the stationary figure and high for the fast-changing chase). Furthermore, the data rate required by a particular channel will vary with time, as the nature of the content changes. To cope with this, and to exploit the available bandwidth efficiently, a technique is employed in which the bandwidth is not shared equally among the various channels. In effect, more bits per second are allocated (temporarily) to the channels that need them. This general technique is called **dynamic capacity allocation**.

dynamic capacity allocation

I'll explore this idea a little more, and to do this I need to introduce some aspects of the European Digital Video Broadcasting (DVB) standard. Under this standard, the data for seven or eight TV channels is transmitted at a rate of 40 Mbps in what is known as a 'transport stream'. A transport stream is made up of packets, each 188 bytes long.

Most of the data in the transport stream is derived from a number of so-called 'elementary streams'. An elementary stream might be, for example, an MPEG-encoded audio or video output. To keep things simple, I'll consider combining data from just two elementary streams into one transport stream. First, suppose that the data rates required by each elementary stream are roughly equal. Then the transport stream will consist of packets derived more or less equally from each elementary stream, as shown in Figure 10(a). (Because transport stream packets are small, it is normal for several consecutive packets to carry data from the same elementary stream.)

Now consider the situation when one elementary stream requires a higher data rate than the other for some interval of time. This would be the case if one carries video data where the action is fast and the other corresponds to an image of 'talking heads' – or if one is video and the other is audio. In these cases, the higher-rate elementary stream is allocated a higher proportion of transport stream packets than the lower-rate stream. This is illustrated in principle in Figure 10(b), although the precise way in which the packets are allocated is complex, and depends very much on the nature of the elementary streams involved.

In a practical situation there are more than two elementary streams making up a transport stream. Furthermore, in addition to video and audio data, there is timing and synchronisation data. There is also a great

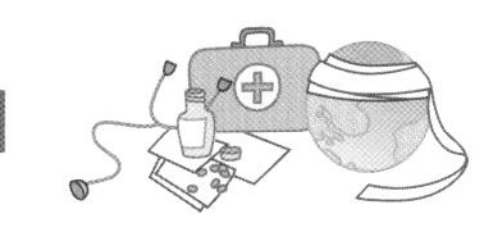

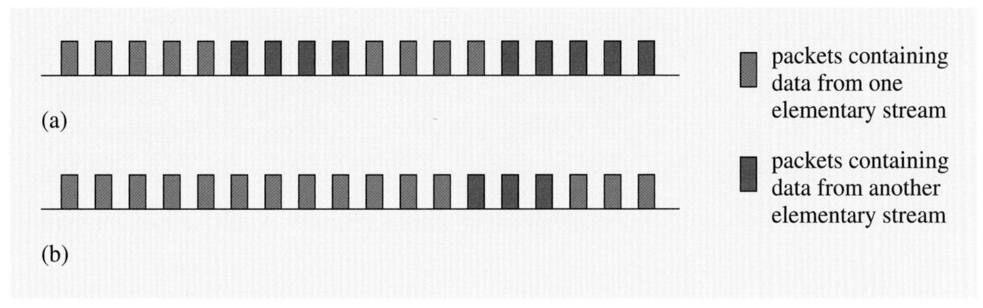

Figure 10 (a) A transport stream shared approximately equally between data from two elementary streams (shown in red and blue); (b) a transport stream where a higher proportion of packets derive from one of two elementary streams

deal of control information that keeps track of the source and nature of the elementary streams as they are broken up at the transmitter in order to form the transport stream packets, and then reconstituted at the receiver.

Before I leave this topic of digital television I should mention one final point. A further advantage of digital TV over analogue is that of quality: when digital data is degraded as a result of a transmission process it is usually possible to regenerate it perfectly. This is not the case with analogue transmission. On the other hand, digital TV tends to be 'all or nothing'. If a point is reached where any degradation can no longer be corrected, then a sudden loss of adequate picture or sound quality is the result. Analogue TV, in contrast, tends to 'degrade gracefully': the picture or sound quality declines gradually as reception conditions worsen.

Activity 8 (self-assessment)

Check your understanding of the way in which 'a great number of [...] digital channels can be packed into the same broadcasting band as was used for a few analogue ones' by filling in the gaps in the following.

The two ideas that are exploited to pack in the digital channels are ________________ and ________________.

In ________________ the available ________________ is not necessarily allocated equally among all the channels. Instead, a channel with, say, a fast-changing picture will be allocated a higher ________________ of the available ________________ than one with a picture that is changing more slowly.

Comment

The answer is given at the end of this part.

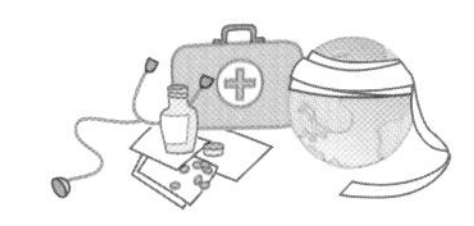

2.5 The internet

The fourth and final ICT system for communicating health information that I shall be discussing is a familiar one: the internet. I'll start by looking at how widespread access to the internet is around the world.

Access

The website that you used in Activity 3 provides data on internet use per 100 inhabitants in the countries of the world. I have used some of this data to produce the bar chart in Figure 11, which compares internet users for Bangladesh, China, Denmark and Uganda from 1999 to 2003. (If you have the time, you might like to revisit the site and look at more recent data.)

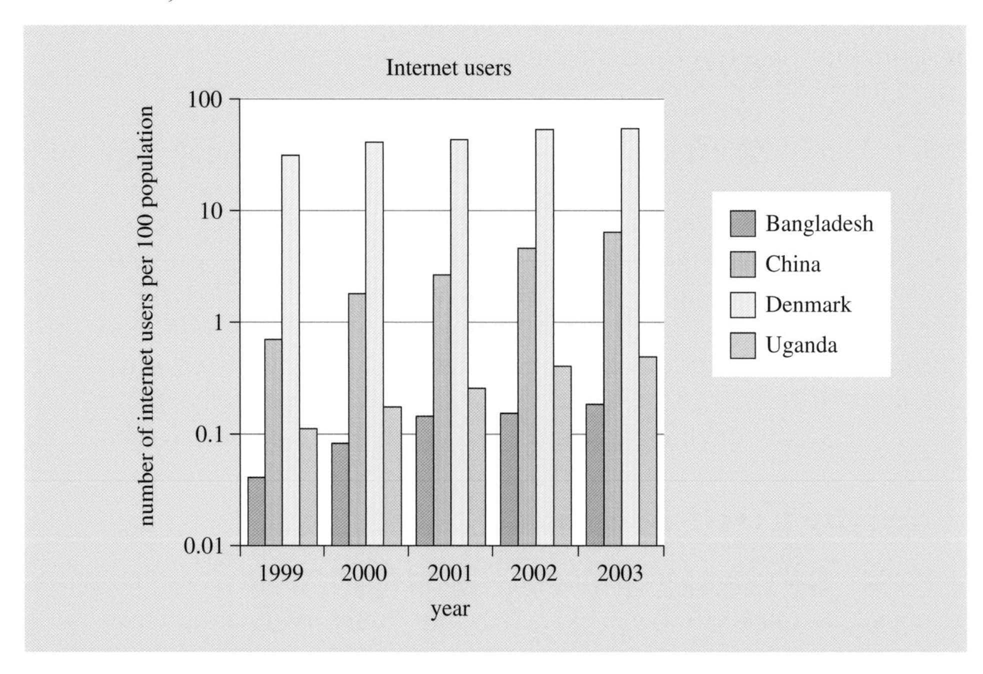

Figure 11 A comparison, using a logarithmic scale, of internet users per 100 inhabitants from 1999 to 2003 for Bangladesh, China, Denmark and Uganda

Activity 9 (self-assessment)

Examine the data in Figure 11. Also look back to Figure 2.

(a) For the year 2003, how do the numbers of internet users per 100 inhabitants in the four countries compare with the numbers of telephone lines/cellular subscribers per 100 inhabitants? Are there any striking differences across the four countries?

(b) How do the trends of internet usage in the four countries compare with the trends in telephone lines/cellular subscribers?

Comment

My answer is given at the end of this part.

Perhaps not surprisingly, given the dependence of internet access on telephones, the data for internet access in the two poorest countries, Bangladesh and Uganda, shows the same stark contrast with the data for Denmark as did the data for phone access. So no matter how much useful health information the Web may offer, a high proportion of the people in these two countries will be unable to access it. China is an unusual case. You saw in Activity 9 that internet use is growing fast there, and I happen to know from various articles I have seen about China recently that there are many internet cafés in Chinese cities. So internet use in China may even catch up with use in Denmark before too long.

Health information via the internet

For those who have access to the internet, the Web provides a rich resource for health-related information. People may look for information on the Web before, after or instead of a consultation with their doctor or a specialist.

Activity 10 (exploratory)

Why do you think you might use the Web before, after or instead of consulting a doctor?

Comment

My answer is given below; you may have thought of different reasons.

Before: researching the topic would help me to ask the doctor more sensible questions, especially if the doctor's diagnosis turned out to confirm my own suspicions.

Instead of: if my search provided me with sufficient reassurance, I might decide that a visit to the doctor was not needed after all. (But this might be a risky strategy – see Activity 11.)

After: I might wish to look up further details about a diagnosis or treatment options.

Seeking out information about a health condition can, however, have drawbacks as well as benefits, especially when the enquirer has no medical background.

Activity 11 (exploratory)

What do you think would be the main drawbacks of using the internet to obtain information about health-related problems, as a substitute for consulting a doctor?

Comment

My answer follows; you may have thought of other points.

The abundance of information can be overwhelming. It may be difficult to select information that is specific to your needs and that is expressed in plain, as opposed to specialist, terms.

The bias of some information may be questionable, so you would need to check each source. For example, some sites are owned or sponsored by companies, who have a vested interest in the content of their pages.

You might make a misdiagnosis of a problem you were experiencing, or misunderstand how to treat it, with potentially serious consequences.

As my comments on Activity 11 imply, being 'informed' means not only having access to information but being able to use it effectively. An abundance of information can make selection of relevant information more difficult. For some people this can lead to an increased level of stress, especially when confronted by many possible ailments that they believe could apply to themselves. The term 'cyberchondriac' has been coined to describe people who become excessively anxious as a result of online searching on health matters. Given the World Health Organization's definition of health, such anxiety is not consistent with a complete state of well-being.

There are many other issues that arise when lay people take on the role of a professional in a specialist subject area, and one of these – the ability to use information effectively – is one I shall be introducing shortly.

2.6 Comparing the media

One way of comparing the effectiveness of ICT systems for communicating health information is to think in terms of information 'push' and information 'pull'.

A common example of information push is the viewing of a conventional television programme. Once the user has switched the television on and selected the channel to be viewed, the programme or advertisements that are running at the time are pushed into the user's home. The user can exercise choice only by changing channels or switching off (though some choice can be exercised by recording a programme to substitute for programmes that are of less interest). In this example, and in information push in general, the user generally plays a fairly passive role.

A common example of information pull is a visit to a library to find some information. Here the user needs to go to the library (information source) and select the information required from a wide range of resources, including, perhaps, asking the librarian for advice. The user can then select what to read, and in what order, in the chosen book or

journal. The user may already need to know a little about the subject in order to conduct their search effectively. All of this requires the user to be active and selective, which is typical of information pull.

As regards ICT systems, information push is associated with those systems which are one-way; those that are two-way can support information pull. Figure 12 illustrates this; the one-way system in Figure 12(a) supports only information push, while the two-way system in Figure 12(b) allows the user to interact with the information source and so supports information pull.

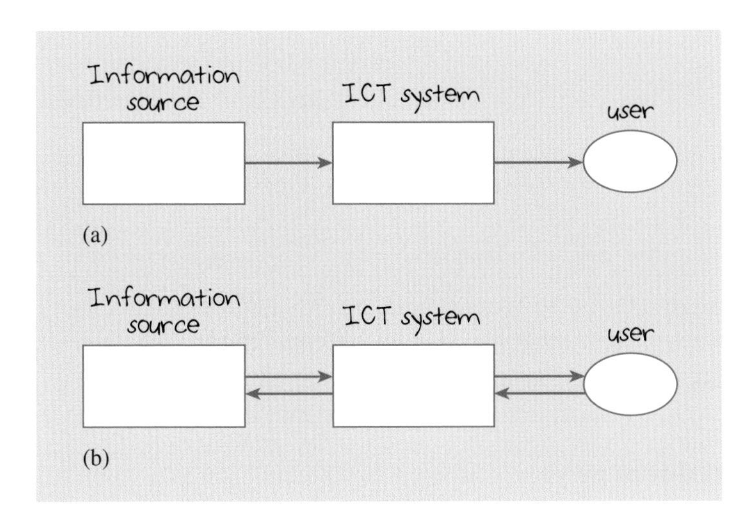

Figure 12 (a) A one-way ICT system offering only information push; (b) a two-way system able to support information pull

Activity 12 (exploratory)

Which sort of information transfer, push or pull, do you think is more likely to meet a user's needs?

Comment

In information push the user does not select the information provided, so it is less likely to satisfy a user's particular need. However, it may serve to bring important information to a user's awareness, so it could still fulfil a need.

With information pull the user is involved in the selection of the information and so the information is more likely to meet a user's particular needs.

In using the idea of information push or pull you shouldn't expect to be able to categorise all information transfer as wholly one or wholly the other. However, just identifying whether an ICT system is more strongly information push or information pull can provide the basis for

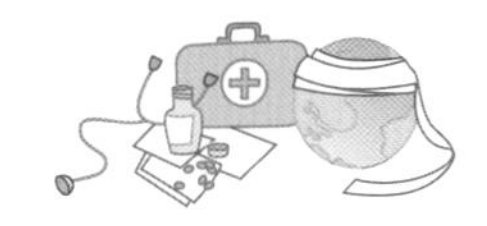

an analysis of its potential usefulness. The next activity provides you with an opportunity to apply the ideas behind information push and pull to some of the ICT systems that you have met in this section.

Activity 13 (self-assessment)

Identify the elements of information push and information pull when the following ICT systems are used for delivering health-related information:

(a) telephone used to phone NHS Direct

(b) broadcast radio

(c) the internet used to access the Web

(d) digital TV used to access NHS Direct Interactive.

Comment

My answer is given at the end of this part.

Activity 13 will have reminded you that the UK's NHS Direct service is available via three different ICT systems: the telephone, digital TV (NHS Direct Interactive) and the internet (NHS Direct Online). In Activity 14 I shall ask you to compare these three branches of NHS Direct.

Activity 14 (exploratory)

The T175 website gives a link to the NHS Direct Online in the Block 4 section of the Resources page. Spend a few minutes looking at the online version of NHS Direct. Based on your impressions of NHS Direct Online, and on my descriptions of accessing NHS Direct Interactive using digital television (see Section 2.4) and accessing NHS Direct using the telephone (see Section 2.2), what do you think would be the main strengths and weaknesses of each form of NHS Direct for you, as a user of the service? (Ignore the issue of information push or pull, which has already been covered in Activity 13.) What skills would you need to access each form of NHS Direct? Arrange your ideas as short notes in a table similar to Table 1.

Table 1 Comparison of strengths, weaknesses and skills needed for access in the three forms of NHS Direct

	Strengths	Weaknesses	Skills needed
Telephone			
Digital TV			
Internet			

Comment

My answer is shown in Table 2, but you may have made different, and equally valid, points.

Table 2 Comparison of strengths, weaknesses and skills needed for access in the three forms of NHS Direct

	Strengths	Weaknesses	Skills needed
Telephone	Most people have access to a telephone. Personal interaction – important when concerned about health. Nurse can lead patient to obtain further evidence.	May not remember all that is said, so need to make notes to refer to afterwards.	Ability and confidence to converse with unknown and unseen nurse.
Digital TV	Will be widely available (once analogue services are withdrawn and people switch to digital). TV set usually conveniently to hand.	Television screens are designed to be viewed from a distance, so information may be constrained to few words with large text. May need to make notes for reference afterwards. TV may not be available for individual use.	Familiarity with specific control functions of a digital remote control. (Remember the difficulties of programming a video recorder?)
Internet	Plenty of resources. Enquirer leads search. (Maybe these are weaknesses too?) Can print out information.	Cost of equipment and subscription to internet services (or relatively inconvenient access in a library or internet café). May be overwhelmed with information, some of it conflicting. May not understand information and advice given. Could be slow if no broadband.	Ability to use a computer and search web pages.

The service offered via digital TV is, at the time of writing, the least accessible to UK citizens, as many people still use analogue television services. However, there are plans to move wholly to digital television in the UK by 2012, so we can assume that access to digital TV will grow rapidly over the next few years. Television has a wider user profile in demographic terms than has the internet. Therefore the fact that digital television is one of the options should considerably increase access to NHS Direct.

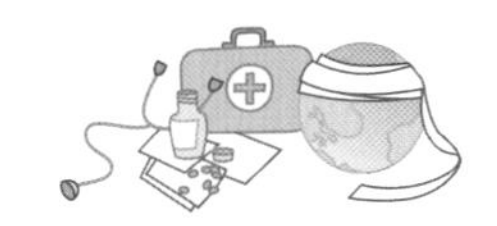

2.7 Making use of information

So far in Section 2 I have been concerned with the use of ICT systems to communicate health information. However, people do not always find it easy to use the information they have received effectively, especially where judgements have to be made. This section therefore focuses on making use of information, and in particular on making judgements about use of information.

In the developed world, life expectancy is increasing but this also increases the demand on health services. Governments may encourage citizens to take a greater responsibility for looking after their own health. The term 'patient empowerment' is often used to promote this idea. But to what extent can people use information they receive to reach sound decisions regarding their own health?

A doctor deciding what treatment might be best for a patient would need to consider a whole range of factors, such as genetic make-up, family history, home environment, existing condition and medical history. Every patient's profile will be different, and this will affect the treatment given. Further, medical opinion itself is not static but often changes, especially when research programmes announce new findings. Medical decision making is therefore based upon professional judgement and experience and the prevailing medical evidence.

There is no substitute for training and experience in matters like this, but sometimes the concept of probability can help. For instance, if you know from clinical trials that Treatment A has a 75% chance of curing a particular problem, whereas treatment B has a 40% chance, you would probably decide to go with Treatment A, at least in the first instance.

Probability

probability

Because knowing the **probability** – that is, the likelihood – of various outcomes can help in decision making I am going to focus on the concept of probability in this subsection. I'll start with examples where probabilities are more clear-cut than they tend to be in health-related matters.

If you toss a coin, there are just two possible outcomes: heads or tails. As these two outcomes are equally likely the probability of getting heads on a coin-toss is 1 in 2, or 1/2, or 0.5, or 50%. And similarly the probability of getting tails is 1 in 2, or 1/2, or 0.5, or 50%.

Similarly, if you throw a dice there are just six possible outcomes: you throw a 1, or 2, or ... up to 6. Again all the outcomes are equally probable, so the probability of throwing, say, a 4 is 1 in 6, or 1/6, or 0.167 (to three significant figures) or 16.7% (again to three significant figures).

Probabilities are normally expressed as a decimal fraction. Thus the probability of tossing a coin and getting heads is expressed as 0.5 and the probability of throwing a dice and getting a 4 is expressed as 0.167 (to three significant figures).

A probability of 0 represents an event which is a complete impossibility, and a probability of 1 represents an event which is a complete certainty. All other probability values lie between these two extremes and represent various degrees of certainty.

Here's another example. You rummage (without looking) in a drawer for a blue ballpoint pen. If there are four black, one red and three blue pens, then the probability of getting a blue pen is 3 in 8 because, of the eight pens, three are blue. Hence the probability of getting a blue pen is 3/8, which works out to 0.375. This assumes that you can't distinguish between the pens by 'feel', of course. If you can, then the probability of getting a blue pen will be higher.

You can see from all these examples that the rule for working out the probability is to divide the total number of favourable, or desired, or specified outcomes by the total number of possible outcomes. Try this in the next activity.

Activity 15 (self-assessment)

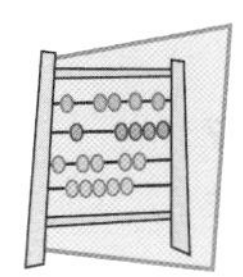

In the situation with the pens just described, and before any pens are taken out, what is the probability of getting:

(a) The red pen?

(b) A black pen?

Again, assume you neither look in the drawer nor work by 'feel' to distinguish the pens.

Comment

The answer is given at the end of this part.

Sometimes probabilities need to be combined in order to deduce an overall probability of an event occurring. For example, suppose you are rummaging in the drawer not just for a pen but also for a pad of paper. If there are two pads, one lined and one plain, what is the probability that you will pick up a blue pen and a lined pad? You already know that the probability of picking up a blue pen is 0.375. As there are just two pads, the probability of picking the lined one must be 0.5. To find the probability of picking a blue pen *and* a lined pad you simply multiply the two probabilities. So the probability is $0.375 \times 0.5 = 0.1875$. You may find it easier to interpret this result if you think of it as a bit less than 0.2, which is 1 in 5.

A word of caution: it is possible to multiply probabilities in this way only if the two events are independent of each other – that is, they have no influence on each other. Here the pen that you pull out does not influence the pad you pull out, or vice versa, so the two events are indeed independent. Provided the events are independent, the rule is: to find the probability of Event A *and* Event B happening, *multiply* the probability of Event A by the probability of Event B. The rule holds whether the two events are more or less simultaneous (as in pulling a pen and pad out of a drawer), or whether one event happens some time after the other (as in pulling a pen out today and a pad tomorrow – provided no one has tampered with the drawer's contents in between!)

Sometimes probabilities are added. For example, during a board game, such as Snakes and Ladders, there may be a positive outcome awaiting you (a ladder to climb) if you throw a 5 *or* if you throw a 1. What is the probability that you throw one of these two numbers? The answer is that you add their two probabilities: $0.167 + 0.167 = 0.334$ (to three significant figures). You can see that this is correct as follows: of the six possible outcomes of throwing a dice, two give desirable outcomes in this case. So the probability of getting a desirable outcome is 2 divided by 6, which is 0.333 (to three significant figures). Don't worry about the discrepancy in the final digit here – it comes from rounding 0.16666666... to 0.167.

Again a word of caution: it is possible to add probabilities of two events in this way only if the events are mutually exclusive – that is, the two events cannot occur simultaneously. Here throwing a 5 precludes throwing a 1, and vice versa, so the two events are indeed mutually exclusive. Provided the events are mutually exclusive, the rule is that to find the overall probability of either Event A *or* Event B *add* their probabilities together.

Notice if you add the probability of getting heads on a coin-toss (0.5) to the probability of getting tails (0.5) you get 1. This is because a coin toss must give either heads or tails; there is no other outcome, and so they are mutually exclusive. Hence the two probabilities must add to 1.

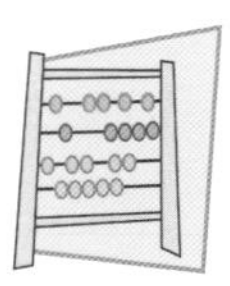

Activity 16 (self-assessment)

You may find a calculator useful for some parts of this activity.

(a) In the pens-in-a-drawer situation you worked with in Activity 15, what is the probability that you withdraw either a black pen or a blue pen?

(b) Suppose that you are playing a board game that involves throwing a dice to progress round the board. If you land on some of the squares you are directed to draw a card from a stack of 15 cards. At one stage of this game you will collect some bonus points if you throw a 2 and then draw one particular card from the stack.

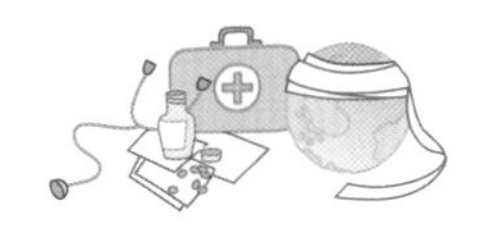

(i) What is the probability of throwing a 2?

(ii) What is the probability of drawing one particular card from a stack of 15?

(iii) What is the probability of getting the bonus points?

(c) At one stage of the above board game, the probability of your losing a large number of points on the next throw of the dice is 0.02. What is the probability of your *not* losing these points on the next throw?

Comment

The answer is given at the end of this part.

The ideas about probability you have just met can be used in a technique known as a 'decision tree' in order to help in decision making in all sorts of circumstances, including health-related circumstances. There is an activity on the DVD relating to decision trees.

You should now run the interactive animation on the T175 course DVD called 'Decision trees'. You are likely to need to use a calculator during this activity.

Although the activity on the DVD is about a doctor calculating probabilities, in practice it is very unlikely that a doctor would work exactly in this way. Doctors are more likely to use a mixture of training and experience to arrive at their decisions, but of course their training and experience will have given them a feel for the likelihood (an informal word for 'probability') of certain outcomes, and they will bring this to bear in reaching a decision. Computer-based 'expert systems' have been developed, and when used to support medical decision making they work much more mathematically, and hence in a way much closer to the decision tree you have just met.

As a final point I should add that I have simplified many of the ideas that I have used in decision making because I wanted to introduce you to the general ideas without getting into too many details. Decision making would normally need to include many more factors, including the emotional aspects of such decisions.

2.8 Summary of Section 2

In this section I have been considering how people can access health-related information using ICT systems. I started by discussing the issue of access, and showed that there are three significant aspects to it: skill, cost and availability. I then went on to look at four different ICT systems

that can be used to communicate health information: telephones, broadcast radio, digital television and the internet. My treatment of these four ICT systems was centred on three aspects: access issues, what sort of health-related information could be communicated and (except in the case of the internet) some relevant aspects of the underlying technology.

I then went on to introduce the idea that broadcast radio is predominantly an 'information push' medium, but the other three can be used, to varying extents, for 'information pull'.

Along the way, I introduced you to the three branches of the UK's NHS Direct service: the telephone service, the digital TV service (NHS Direct Interactive) and the internet service (NHS Direct Online) and towards the end of the section I asked you to compare their strengths and weaknesses.

Finally, I turned to the issue of making use of the information obtained through these various ICT systems, and that led me to the topic of probability. Here you gained a basic understanding of probability so that you could see how probabilities could be used in a health-related decision tree.

Activity 17 (self-assessment)

To confirm that you have grasped some of the access issues I have discussed, create a copy of Table 3 and write in each row a difference between access to ICT systems in developing countries and access in developed countries. For example, under 'Telephones' you might write that there are much higher numbers of telephone lines and cellular subscribers in developed countries than in developing ones (I suggest you think of another example in this category when completing the table).

Table 3 Differences between access in developing and developed countries

	A difference between access in developing countries and access in developed countries
Telephones	
Broadcast radio	
The internet	

Comment

My answer is given at the end of this part.

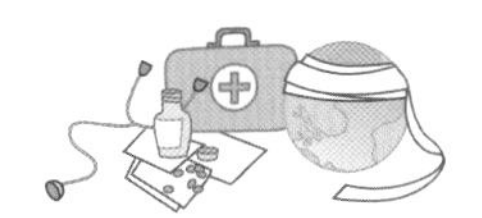

3 Telemedicine

3.1 Introduction

You will need the following resources while studying this section:

- *your computer with internet access for Activity 20.*

telemedicine

Telemedicine literally means *medicine at a distance* (although you will also find the term used in the very general sense of 'the application of information and communication technologies to the practice of healthcare'). In this section, though, the emphasis is on how, in the field of medicine, ICTs can make the world seem a smaller place. I shall also be concerned to some extent with the local use of ICT systems for medical procedures.

In telemedicine, ICT systems can bring medical assistance and expertise to individuals, reducing or even removing the need to transport people to medical centres and hospitals. Transporting patients over long distances when they are not well is undesirable, time-consuming, and probably expensive. In many countries the general transport and medical infrastructure to move patients for treatment may well not exist: roads may be poor, and hospitals and medical staff few and far between. Even in urban environments and in developed countries there are advantages in reducing the number of people needing to visit centres such as clinics and hospitals.

Telemedicine can offer a means by which a doctor's skills are not tied to the physical presence of the doctor. It can also provide some automated medical options such as the remote monitoring of a patient's condition.

Activity 18 (exploratory)

I'd like you to begin by thinking of a fairly routine visit to a doctor's surgery or a clinic. What sorts of thing happen? What does the doctor or nurse listen to or look at? What sorts of discussion take place?

Now, what could you do using the sort of ICT equipment that you might have in a home or a small-office environment, to provide a similar level of information exchange while avoiding an actual visit?

Comment

When I visit my doctor I first describe the reason for my visit and the problems that are concerning me. Instead of this initial face-to-face description I could make a telephone call, or send a written description of the problem by email. But once I've explained the problem, the discussion becomes interactive: my doctor asks me questions, and I respond, so email would not be ideal. Synchronous communication such as the telephone or instant messaging could help.

In the surgery my doctor may carry out routine checks using a stethoscope to listen to sounds generated inside the body (e.g. heartbeat, wheeziness in breathing). Given a suitably sensitive microphone, sound can be recorded as a computer file and attached to an email message, so perhaps I could use this arrangement to replace a stethoscope. But would I know how to do it properly?

Checking blood pressure is another routine procedure. This could only be done remotely if I had more specialised equipment, and felt competent to use it.

Doctors also carry out visual inspections to search for evidence of problems. A digital camera could be used to capture images that may be relevant to my concern. These can be stored as graphics files and transferred over communication networks.

Let's consider now what other technological implications there might be for such a 'teleconsultation'.

First of all, thinking about sound files: a transducer (to convert the audible signal to an electrical signal) with an amplifier (to make it sufficiently loud) could allow sounds to be fed into a standard telephone circuit directly. But as you will know if you have listened to music played on a standard telephone circuit, the quality of sound is restricted by the limited bandwidth of the telephone channel. So if we are to transmit the sounds normally picked up by stethoscope via some sort of communications link, we'll have to ensure that low-frequency thuds (heartbeats) and high-frequency wheezes (lungs) could still be detected.

Thinking next about capturing and sending images: a doctor might need to examine the state of eyes, tongue, skin conditions (such as dermatitis), or injuries and burns. Comparatively inexpensive digital cameras can now produce quite high-quality images, so images suitable for medical examination could be loaded onto a computer for transmitting to a doctor (bearing in mind any safety implications, such as avoiding flash for close-up pictures of faces). Digital cameras that are integrated into mobile phones generally produce lower-quality pictures, but even these can assist in diagnosis. For example, nurses in the UK have trialled the use of camera phones in this way.

A webcam is another possibility for sending images. Webcams are inexpensive cameras that are used for providing low- to medium-quality images for web pages. They can also allow a level of video conferencing. A video conference facility could be useful in discussing some conditions with a doctor, but satisfactory video conferencing may only be possible if a connection with a sufficiently high bit rate is available. In a medical context a video link could be of real benefit. For example, a doctor monitoring a remote patient's heartbeat or blood pressure might need to check for correct positioning of the chest or arm probes.

There are also much simpler examples of potential uses of ICT systems in telemedicine. For example, one low-cost, but potentially very effective, way of using ICTs in healthcare is to exploit text messaging on mobile phones. Text messages can be sent to remind patients of appointments, or to communicate test results. With slight modifications, mobile phones can even be used to send the results of tests carried out by the patient at home to a doctor or hospital.

The aim of all this was to encourage you to think about possibilities. In the rest of this section I shall look in more detail at how ICT systems in practice are bringing together medical specialists, patients, and others at a distance. I shall begin with two contrasting examples that make fairly modest demands on the ICT infrastructure – one from India, one from the UK. Then I shall briefly consider the 'higher tech' end of the spectrum: robotic 'telesurgery'. Finally I'll review some of the ICT network implications for telemedicine.

3.2 Telemedicine on a budget

Please begin by reading the following extract. Note that it refers to ISDN (Integrated Services Digital Network), which is an early form of broadband provision.

India: Telemedicine's Great New Frontier

G. Harris

April, 2002

IEEE Spectrum

[T]elemedicine has undergone something of a resurgence, as technology has begun catching up with aspirations. Perhaps nowhere is this renaissance so vitally needed as in India.

With their dependence on high-bandwidth, real-time technologies, most telemedicine projects of the past decade have been ill-suited to India. Now, though, new hopes are being engendered there by the confluence of low-bandwidth telemedicine with a growing middle class, an improving telecommunications infrastructure, a world-class software industry, and a medical community open to new ideas.

[...]

Can telemedicine really make a difference in India? Two recent events suggest it can. The Gujurat earthquake on 27 January 2001 devastated the western city of Bhuj and left thousands of dead and many more homeless. Within 24 hours the Online Telemedicine Research Institute (OTRI) in Ahmedabad, about 300 km from Bhuj, had established satellite telephone links between an emergency command center in neighbouring Ghandinaghar and various facilities around Bhuj, including one housed in a tent.

In one month, the hook-up transmitted to specialists in Ahmedabad approximately 750 sessions involving primarily X-rays and electrocardiographs of patients in the disaster area. After two days, the satellite phones gave way to the more economical V-SAT (which requires a 2-meter dish), with phone lines and ISDN [Integrated Services Digital Network] being added as infrastructure was repaired. Much of the imaging and data transfer was mediated by Pentium 3 based PCs. [...]

The second encouraging project was carried out during the Kumbh Mela, a Hindu festival held every 12 years that last year drew 25 million pilgrims to the banks of the Ganges River. Here the OTRI and the Sanjay Gandhi Post Graduate Institute established a station under the sponsorship of the Ministry of Information Technology to monitor levels of cholera-causing bacteria in the river water. Microscope images of samples of microorganisms from the river were transmitted to the Institute's experts in pathology and microbiology for identification and analysis. In addition, radiology and cardiology data was transferred to specialists for the total of 202 pilgrims who fell ill. The project ran for 45 days.

[...]

Activity 19 (exploratory)

What role were the ICTs in the previous extract performing? Did it seem to you that high-tech telemedicine equipment was needed?

Comment

These examples seem to me to be classic cases of ICT systems playing the role of reducing or removing constraints imposed by distance and time. Here they are doing this by bringing together patients and medical experts when and where it would be very difficult, if not impossible, to do this physically (because of the relief work in the earthquake, and the sheer numbers of pilgrims at the Kumbh Mela).

Much of the diagnostic work was achieved by transmitting images, which could be done without the extremely high-tech equipment sometimes associated with telemedicine. It also seems likely that specialists would be able to pool their expertise on difficult cases, and then transmit back a considered opinion, again without the need for high-tech telemedicine equipment.

The previous extract described the use of fairly standard ICT devices and systems for the purposes of telemedicine, in combination with specialised medical equipment at temporary or permanent clinics. However, equipment that is specifically designed for medical monitoring in the home is available from a number of suppliers, and is beginning to find a place in healthcare in countries where greater financial resources are available. The following example comes from a short extract from a press release about equipment called CareCompanion (see Figure 13). With such equipment the demand on the general ICT infrastructure can be minimal, even though quite sophisticated ICT equipment may be required at the patient end. (As you read the extract you may like to

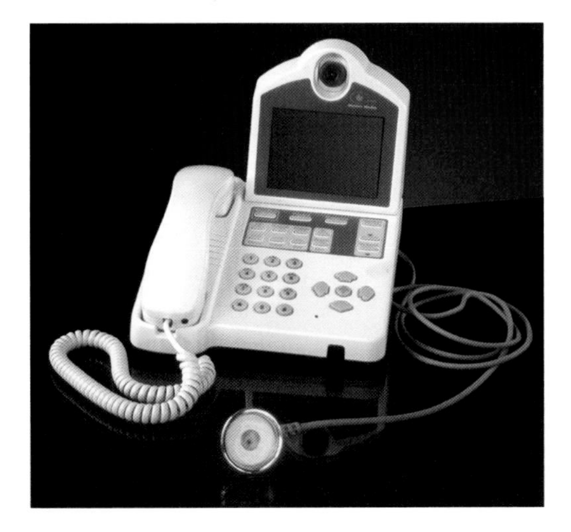

Figure 13 CareCompanion unit with stethoscope

know that an oximeter measures blood oxygen level, and a glucometer measures blood sugar level. Both these measurements can be important indicators of the state of health of a patient.)

> At its most basic configuration, the CareCompanion reminds the client to take medication and asks questions about his/her condition. All interaction between the patient and CareCompanion takes place via a simple touch-screen. After the client completes a session, the CareCompanion automatically delivers its data to [the operating company or clinic] by dialing out on the patient's home phone line. The client's caregiver and physician are given secure access to monitor results and are alerted if the patient's responses fall outside of a range preset by the caregiver.
>
> A variety of vital signs monitors can be added, depending on the patient's specific needs including a blood pressure monitor, weight scale, pulse, oximeter, glucometer and many more.
>
> Home Telehealth Ltd. (2004)

One CareCompanion option, not described in the extract but shown in Figure 13, is to link a stethoscope from patient to doctor via a communications link. In effect, the stethoscope has been divided into two parts, connected by the network. This idea of 'dividing' medical equipment into two parts – one part at the patient end, and one part with the doctor, surgeon or nurse – and using an ICT communications link or network to interconnect them, is an important principle of telemedicine, and I'll return to it later.

When I researched information for this section I noticed that there were many more examples of telemedicine, extending back over many years. For example, in the early years of space exploration there was much interest in the effects of weightlessness on astronauts during prolonged periods of space travel. Monitoring these effects relied upon wireless communications or information recorded during the space flight. More recently there were many examples making use of simple email attachments to carry image files of infected wounds or burns. Emails can be effective for conveying information that isn't time critical.

When telemedicine sessions are required to transmit large amounts of data, and when information is time-sensitive because it is 'live' or several image files are required urgently, network connections may need to be high-speed or 'broadband'. We'll look at this issue later in the section. But first, I'd like you to do a little further investigation of telemedicine yourself.

If it is inconvenient to go online now, just read through my comments to the following activity. But next time you are online, do remember to carry out your own search, and compare your results with mine.

Activity 20 (exploratory)

Find some recent applications of telemedicine across the world. Select three or four examples that have been reported over the last two to three years. The online news sites run by television broadcasters or newspapers might be useful for this. I found many examples through BBC News online. You can enter search terms such as 'telemedicine news', 'remote medical treatment' or 'e-medicine' (a term used in the USA) to find examples from this site. Note down the main results using the format of Table 4. Think about the type of ICT needed – ready-made or specialised; low or high bit rate; etc.

To start you off, I have shown an example in Table 4.

Table 4 An example of telemedicine in the news

Date, place and source	Medical purpose	Use made of ICTs employed	Benefits
Middlesex, England BBC News online, (Elliot, 2003)	Monitoring cystic fibrosis patients after lung transplants.	'Special TV' used by patient to interface with a test facility; telephone for the initial contact; computer. Measurements of breathing, heart rate and temperature.	Allows patients to be monitored in their home environment for several months after treatment.

Comment

I found the examples shown in Table 5 while I was preparing this material.

Table 5 Telemedicine in the news

Date, place and source	Medical purpose	Use made of ICTs employed	Benefits
Bangalore, Southern India BBC News online (Haviland, 2003)	Patients receive specialist heart advice normally only accessible in major centres.	Satellite links and terrestrial 128 kbps links to access specialist help. Various images such as X-rays and heart-related cardiographs were sent.	Specialist receives data needed to diagnose problems. Most patients don't need operations, so needless long-distance travel by patients avoided.
Guam – a Pacific Island ZDNet (Borland and Hu, 2004)	Cardiac surgical procedure at a military hospital. Supervisory surgeon 3500 miles away.	Real-time transmission of heart pressure data. High-resolution video link over high-speed links.	Less-experienced medics could perform surgical procedures under remote supervision. Transportation of patient to specialist unnecessary.
USA NASA News Release (NASA,2004)	Use of telemedicine projects to gain experience for long-distance missions to Mars.	Wireless links – the only option for space travel. High-specification computers overcome difficulties of very long transmission paths on journey to Mars.	Experiences used to help doctors train space crews to perform surgery under weightless conditions aboard a plummeting aircraft!
India Wireless Healthcare (2005)	Medical aid to tsunami victims. Linking mobile teams of rescue workers with hospitals and medical centres.	'Portable Telemedicine Work Stations' and 'Compact Data Terminals' used with satellite communication systems in place of damaged infrastructure networks.	Doctors and paramedics able to treat victims locally while maintaining close contact with mobile 'field' and permanent hospitals.

Here is one final thought about the sort of telemedicine we have been looking at in this section. Telemedicine is not simply about the technology; there are also important human issues. For example, a relationship, however temporary, is normally established between a patient and a doctor. It remains to be seen whether patients' confidence and trust can be established where ICT networks are used to give treatment by people that they may never meet.

3.3 Telesurgery

I'm now going to move on to a more specialised area of telemedicine – that of telesurgery. Telesurgery, as you will have probably guessed, is surgery at a distance – though as you will see later, the distances don't have to be great. Telesurgery may seem an unlikely proposition at first sight, but there have been some interesting developments in the area and it has been shown to be a practical option for a growing number of procedures.

Telesurgery is closely related to robotic surgery – though you should be clear that here we are talking about robotic mechanisms under direct human supervision rather than robots that can carry out activities autonomously. This sort of operation has much to do with an alternative to conventional surgery that is named 'minimally invasive' surgery or 'keyhole' surgery.

Minimally invasive surgery has developed significantly over recent decades. It uses only small access areas (referred to as 'ports') to the body's interior. The advantage of this approach is that the physical and emotional disturbances associated with conventional surgery (where larger incisions are made) are minimised. This results in reduced post-operative pain and improved healing times.

Minimally invasive surgery is carried out using equipment outside the body to move and manipulate surgical instruments, or tools, inside the body. This requires mechanisms such as robotic assemblies and control systems that allow a surgeon to carry out precise manoeuvres of the miniaturised surgical instruments. The term 'micromanipulation' captures the essence of this type of activity.

The surgeon's view of the internal activity is limited to images obtained from endoscopes. These are instruments within the body that relay images, usually from an optical fibre probe, for display on a video monitor.

Surgeons working in this field already work in a 'remote' manner: for much of the operating time they will be relying on intermediate, robot-assisted systems rather than on direct physical contact with the part of the patient they are operating on. Extending the distances involved from a metre or two to thousands of kilometres would allow a surgeon on one side of the world to operate on a patient on the other. In effect, the robot-assisted system is divided into two parts, interconnected by a telecommunications channel – rather like the stethoscope in the CareCompanion example.

Such telesurgery has already been carried out over very long distances. For example, the first transatlantic telesurgical procedure was carried out in 2001. A patient in Strasbourg, France, had her gall bladder removed by a surgical team in New York, USA.

What are the implications of such procedures? Read the following short extract; Figure 14, just after the extract, shows two views of the Zeus robotic surgical system that it mentions.

Extending Healthcare's Reach

S.K. Moore

January, 2002

IEEE Spectrum

[...] For the transatlantic procedure Marescaux [the surgeon, based in New York] used a Zeus robotic surgical system, developed by Computer Motion, Inc., Goleta, California. In point of fact, Zeus's two major components, a central console and a three-armed robot, were designed to be located together in an operating room. The surgeon moves controls on the end of two arms at a console; these movements are translated to the two robot arms manipulating surgical instruments [...] The third arm maneuvres a video camera [...]

[...]

In many applications of telemedicine, as elsewhere, bandwidth is the limiting factor. That was not the case in the New York to Strasbourg surgery. [...] Both voice-over Internet protocol (VoIP), for Marescaux to communicate with the personnel at the patient's side, and high-quality video were transmitted, 10 Mbps of data in all. But that was easily handled by the network supplied for the surgery by France Telecom, Paris. Instead, the time it took a signal to travel from the console in New York City to the robot in Strasbourg and back – the latency – proved the most critical aspect of the network technology.

Indeed, until the September surgery, latency was expected to put what the surgeon sees at the controls too far out of synch with events on the operating table for the technique to be used beyond a distance of about 300 km. Experiments by Marescaux's group found that any latency greater than 250 ms was dangerous, but engineers at Computer Motions and France Telecom compressed it to just 155 ms [...] A full 70 ms of the latency was taken up by the video coding and decoding from the endoscopic camera. [...]

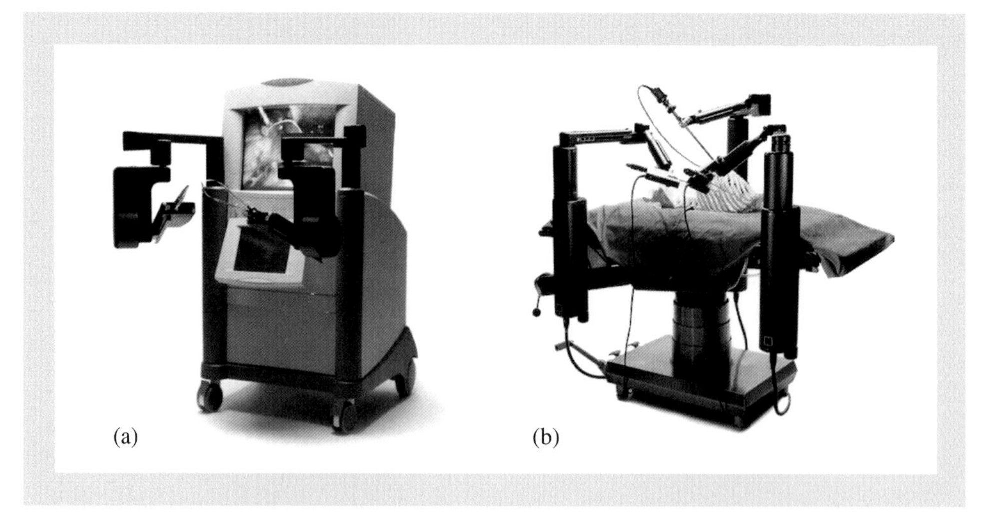

Figure 14 A Zeus robotic surgery system: (a) the surgeon's console; (b) the remotely operated arms to hold instruments and the video feed

In the above extract, the author uses the term 'latency'. This is a term whose meaning is changing. Increasingly, it is being used simply as a synonym for 'delay', and you will find it used in this way in many articles about ICTs. But strictly 'latency' means the *total* delay along a signal's path. This total delay will include the travelling time of the signal, known as the 'propagation delay', and any delay due to the data being manipulated (for example during compression and decompression) and any delay due to the temporary storage of the data. Sometimes a one-way path is of interest, and then the latency will be the total one-way delay. In other cases, as in the above extract, it is the round trip that is of interest, and then the latency will be the total round-trip delay.

Activity 21 (self-assessment)

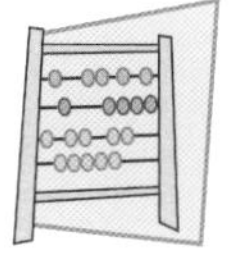

Assume that the round trip from Strasbourg to New York is 10 000 km and that the telesurgery signals propagate through optical fibres at 2×10^8 m/s. Work out the proportion of the quoted latency (total round-trip delay) that was taken up by the propagation delay and the proportion that was taken up by the video coding/decoding.

Comment

The answer is given at the end of this part.

From the answer to the previous activity you will have seen that all but 35 ms of the total round-trip delay is taken up by propagation time and video coding/decoding. The other contributing factor to the total delay is temporary storage in memory (buffering) during the transmission. It seems to me that the system was operating pretty close to practical limits.

At this point, you may be wondering why people have devoted all this effort to perform surgery at a distance. Proponents of such technological developments often cite surgeon training as an important feature. By means of telesurgery, an inexperienced practitioner can work with an expert at a distance. According to Jacques Marescaux (the surgeon who conducted the transatlantic gall bladder operation): 'When a surgeon begins a new operation alone, the first 10–20 operations are on a learning curve, and the complication rate is higher. In the future, if we can suppress that with technology, no one will accept such high rates' (Moore, 2002). But there's always an argument about allocation of resources, and in particular there's a potential conflict between the use of highly advanced technology for new applications, and the use of technology for more conventional, perhaps less exciting ones.

Bearing this in mind, let's look in a little more detail at some 'more advanced' technological issues.

Feedback

The development of robotic assistive surgery of the kind I have described above is dependent upon advances in several fields, such as electronics, mechanical engineering, physics, materials science and ICTs. Such robotic systems exploit the notion of feedback in many ways.

feedback

When we carry out some action with our bodies such as driving a car, riding a bicycle or simply standing upright, we rely upon our body's own feedback mechanisms. By **feedback** I mean checking the result of an action, and then applying the information to subsequent actions – either explicitly, or as part of our bodies' innate mechanisms.

Monitoring the result of an action and then using the information to modify what is going on is also called 'closed-loop control', a concept that will be considered further in Part 2 of this block.

When riding a bicycle – or even simply standing or sitting still – we depend upon several senses to be able to balance correctly without thinking about what we're doing. Often we're completely unaware of the importance of feedback, particularly when we've learnt to do an action that relies upon it.

Our ability to carry out difficult and delicate manipulations of objects relies heavily upon feedback. For example, we can fairly easily learn how to handle an egg directly – although most of us can remember incidents as a child when the learning process resulted in egg on the floor. The feedback in this case includes locating the egg using vision and moving our arm, and sensing how much force we apply, so as not to crack the egg. To handle an egg remotely by means of a robot manipulator the technological device has to apply just sufficient force to overcome the egg's weight and just the right amount of 'grip' to hold it securely without dropping it.

Activity 22 (exploratory)

Imagine that you are a surgeon who, on being newly introduced to robot-assisted surgery of the type that I have described, is thinking about the feedback problem. What major worries might you have?

Comment

As a surgeon, anticipating carrying out a robot-assisted operation, I would worry first about losing the 'feel' of what I was doing. I would need to be certain that when I performed an action (a cut, a manipulation of an organ, and so on), I would be able to apply the right amount of force to achieve what was needed. I would also need to see and feel exactly what I had done clearly. So I would also worry about the quality of the video being used, and the amount of delay in

the system. Any significant delay would affect my ability to respond quickly and properly during an operation. The longer the delay, the longer the feedback will take to reach me, and the less accurate my response is likely to be.

In the context of robotic surgery, then, a surgeon would need to be able to perceive the force being applied by the surgical tools without direct contact with them. The feedback required to do this is termed 'force feedback'. Force feedback involves measuring the force being applied by an instrument and feeding it back to the operator in such a way that it can be felt. This has been a major area of robotics research over many years and is termed 'tactile sensing' – in effect, the measurement and control of touch.

Vision and depth

Being able to see clearly what is being carried out is crucial. This needs well-thought-out arrangements for presenting the best views to a surgeon. For example when performing a cut, can its depth be accurately gauged? In a three-dimensional world this is not normally a problem, but when a view is presented on a flat display screen this sort of detail could be difficult to detect.

One possible approach is to create stereoscopic views by separating the image information for one eye from the image information for the other eye. Virtual-reality systems use this type of approach, but what works well for some people may induce headaches and nausea in others.

Other issues

As you have seen, extending surgery over great distances is certainly possible, although the technological problems are significant.

Activity 23 (exploratory)

Apart from the problems of delay, vision, and force feedback, which we have already considered, what do you think would be the other major concerns involved in extending the sort of robot-assisted surgery that I have described over large distances using ICT networks?

Comment

The reliability of the network connection would be of critical importance over the duration of the procedure, which could be several hours. There would need to be an alternative means of connection should a network failure occur, and reconnection would have to be fast enough not to endanger the patient.

> If complications arose relating to the patient's condition or any of the technical arrangements, there should ideally be a fall-back arrangement or contingency plan, in which human beings close to the patient could take over to cope with any necessary changes. However, the justification for a telesurgical procedure being carried out in the first place would probably be that the best surgeon or equipment was not available at the same place as the patient.

Telesurgery may find application in situations where there are very few real alternatives. For instance, I previously referred to potential medical problems during interplanetary space missions. There has also been an interest in battlefield situations where urgent medical help cannot be provided by normal means. The Trauma Pod project, at the conceptual stage in 2005, has been conceived by the US military under the Defense Advanced Research Projects Agency (the same agency that was involved in the forerunner of the internet). It is described in the following terms:

> When fully developed, the Trauma Pod will not require human medical personnel on-site to conduct the surgery, and will be small enough to be carried by a medical ground or air vehicle. A human surgeon will conduct all the required surgical procedures from a remote location using a system of surgical manipulators. The system's actions are then communicated wirelessly to the surgery site. Automated robotic systems will provide necessary support to the surgeon to conduct all phases of the operation.
>
> PhysOrg (2005)

The arrangement described has much in common with the sort of systems we have been considering, but in a more compact and self-contained environment.

3.4 Broadband for telemedicine

When computers are used with 'dial-up' telephone connections, data can be transmitted or received at a rate of between about 30 and 50 kbps, depending on local conditions. Many applications using ICTs, especially those in which real-time (or 'live') image data is sent, require network connections that can handle much higher data rates. Such connections, especially those to domestic and small-business users, are termed **broadband**, and are clearly of interest in telemedicine applications.

broadband

Early broadband standards were based upon the Integrated Services Digital Network (ISDN) which provided data rates in multiples of 64 kbps. However, services to homes and businesses in industrialised countries are (in 2005) available at several megabits per second.

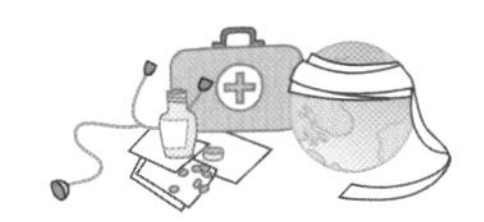

In contrast to traditional modems, broadband connections are generally 'always on', which avoids the inherent unreliability and inconvenient delays of telephone 'dial-up' connections.

Activity 24 (self-assessment)

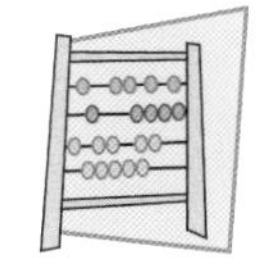

Suppose that a series of compressed image files of the following sizes need to be sent across a 128 kbps link to support an online consultation. How long would it take to send them one after another? Do you think this would be fast enough for a telemedicine application?

280 KB, 980 KB, 420 KB and 730 KB

(Remember that a capital K when used to express a file or memory size refers to 1024, not 1000.)

Comment

The answer is at the end of this part.

Various technologies are available for the provision of broadband to domestic or business customers. I'll outline the main features of two important ones shortly. First, though, note that terms like 'high speed', 'fast' or 'slow', which you will often find used in the context of broadband, can sometimes mislead. Using 'fast' and 'slow' to describe data rates or bit rates is fine, but the idea of speed can mislead you into thinking that the actual signals travel faster. This is incorrect, because the speed of a signal down a copper wire, through an optical fibre or through free space will be a known value depending upon the medium. It will normally lie between 2×10^8 and 3×10^8 m/s. The data rate, on the other hand, will be determined by how fast the signal can change to represent successive bits. For example, signals can change much faster in an optical cable than in a copper cable of the same length without losing quality in the received data.

Digital Subscriber Line (DSL)

Digital Subscriber Line (DSL) is the name for a family of technologies that make best use of the twisted-pair telephone wires connecting most homes to their local switching centre (telephone exchange). DSL technologies achieve high data rates by reducing the effects of noise, using advanced error detection and correction. In addition to supplying broadband to the home, DSL technologies may be a component of large institutional networks, such as the NHS network which will be discussed in Section 4.

Asymmetric Digital Subscriber Line (ADSL)

Asymmetric Digital Subscriber Line (ADSL) is a version of DSL that became widespread in Europe in the early 2000s, and is the most common broadband technology for home access in the UK. The term 'asymmetric' is used because the bit rate is significantly greater for data being sent to a user compared with data sent from the user. This

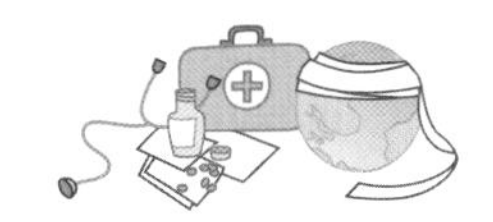

asymmetry is acceptable for browsing web pages or downloading other large files, but less so for users who need to upload large data files.

The data rates offered by service providers increased significantly in the early years of the technology, and the precise rates achievable depend upon the distance between the user and the local switching centre. At the time of writing (2005) data rates of 1 or 2 Mbps are commonly available in Europe to users close to a local exchange.

Broadband to mobile phones

Mobile phone technology has become increasingly oriented towards data as well as voice transmission. 3G (third generation) handsets are capable of downloading data at broadband data rates of around 2 Mbps, but this can reduce to just 144 kbps when a user is in a moving vehicle.

3G data rates can be increased using a technique called 'Multiple Input, Multiple Output (MIMO)'. This is like combining the performance of several individual handsets to achieve a high data rate, but using only a single handset. Multiple antennas are needed in these handsets to allow the necessary data streams to be transmitted or received at the same time. A data rate of 10 Mbps can be achieved using this approach – at a price!

Activity 25 (self-assessment)

Look back at the telemedicine applications described in this section (including my examples in the Activity 20 question and comments). Find one application that falls into each of the following categories:

(a) can operate over a standard telephone line

(b) needs a data rate of 5 Mbps or more.

Comment

My answer is at the end of this part.

Health services in a number of countries are introducing broadband networks for a variety of purposes, including some of the telemedicine applications discussed in this section. We'll look at an example from the UK in Section 4.

3.5 Summary of Section 3

In this section we have looked at some of the technologies that can be used to provide healthcare and treatment when resources and expertise are physically separated from patients. We have looked at what might be possible by exploiting standard ICTs and also very sophisticated robotic surgical systems. Many technical issues arise, and one this section has specifically addressed is that of bandwidth.

4 Networking health

4.1 Introduction

You might recall that in the Introduction to this part of Block 4 I said that one of my areas of concern would be how national health provision is being reshaped around the opportunities provided by ICT systems. This is what we shall look at in this section, concentrating on the UK's National Programme for Information Technology – a large-scale project to use modern ICT systems for medical information and communications within the National Health Service (NHS).

Before looking at the UK, however, we should take account of the wider European context. The UK's policy on many issues is often aligned with international policy, and health service provision is no exception.

In the 'e-Health Action Plan' (European Commission, 2004) the European Commission called upon its member states to produce plans to support a vision of delivering better-quality healthcare to European citizens, with fewer mistakes made and reduced waiting times. The plan envisaged that each citizen of the European Union (EU) would carry a smart health card that would uniquely identify them. The smart card would provide access to the citizen's electronic patient record on a database from anywhere within the EU, and allow the citizen to obtain medication from any pharmacy in the EU.

This EU-wide scheme presupposes that member countries of the European Union have their medical records in electronic form and accessible online, together with there being some form of electronic prescription. These are just two of the objectives of the UK's National Programme for Information Technology.

4.2 National Programme for Information Technology

The UK's National Programme for IT (NPfIT) was initiated in October 2002, following a number of reports and strategy documents in the preceding few years which advocated greater use of information technology within the UK's National Health Service. It is an extremely large project, and is estimated to take ten years to complete. It encompasses the creation of a database of medical records of all UK citizens, called the Care Records Service.

The national database of the Care Records Service holds a summary of care and clinical history for each patient. This is known as the 'spine'. It includes name, address, NHS number and date of birth, and information about allergies, adverse reactions to drugs, etc. In-depth details about treatment are held locally. Links from summary information in the spine enable the locally held information to be accessed.

According to Cross (2004):

> [...] the 'Care Records Service' [...] will enable NHS professionals to call up details of every patient wherever they are needed. The spine carries administrative details of each patient – name, NHS number and so on – together with crucial information such as blood group and allergies. Systems in individual NHS trusts [administrative bodies with responsibility for NHS provision within a particular area] feed the spine with summaries of treatments received throughout the patient's life. The spine also controls security, ensuring that only registered clinicians (and eventually the patients themselves) see clinical data.

Prior to the introduction of this system, medical records have not only been paper-based, but have been held by a patient's GP (general practitioner, the local doctor a patient is assigned to). Thus a doctor attending someone who fell ill on holiday, for instance, would not readily have access to the person's medical records, and updating that person's records to include information on the holiday illness would depend on the attending doctor writing to the person's GP with details of the illness. Understandably, this paper system has come to be seen as rather inefficient, although we should perhaps not be too quick to condemn it. I will say more about this in Section 4.8, when I look at questions of confidentiality.

Creating a database of medical records is only one part of the NPfIT project, however, and we shall look at the other parts in Section 4.4.

As with many large-scale IT projects, great benefits are claimed for the new system. When I consulted a website associated with the project, in July 2005, the benefits were described in the following terms. I have underlined certain phrases that caught my attention, as I often do when reading new material.

> The National Programme for IT [...] is bringing modern computer systems into the NHS to improve patient care and services. Over the next ten years it will connect over 30,000 general practitioners in England to almost 300 hospitals and give patients access to their personal health and care information, transforming the way the NHS works.

> Information will move around more quickly with health care records, appointments, prescription information, and up-to-date research into illnesses and treatments accessible to patients and health professionals whenever they need it.
>
> NHS (2005)

When I think of health services, and especially hospitals, I imagine hi-tech environments, so I wondered why 'modern computer systems' had been singled out for mention. Perhaps the people most involved in patient care and treatment aren't quite as surrounded by modern computer systems as I had first assumed. I recollect that, even quite recently, family members and friends who have had hospital tests have had to wait for the results to be sent by post from hospital to their general practitioner (GP) before learning the outcome of the tests.

Another one: 'give patients access'. This seems admirable, but I thought that I had access to my health records already. I wonder who else may be given access without my knowledge, and am I happy about this?

The word 'transforming' is significant too, I think, because I've come across this before in the field of managing change. Transforming suggests some really big changes in the way things are done. When organisations are transformed the people who are affected can feel uneasy, threatened and upset by the changes that are taking place. I wondered who would be affected and to what extent their roles and responsibilities might change.

Another point that struck me was the emphasis upon the apparent mobility of information ('move around') and the timeliness of its availability ('whenever') (as well as wherever).

When reading statements of this kind, we need to be cautious about whether the information might be biased in some way. The writer might be trying to enthuse us or win over our support for an idea. One aspect that was missing from this statement was any mention of costs. When any organisation implements new technologies, there is usually an analysis of the costs as well as the benefits. The particular site from which the above quotation was taken was an NHS site and was clearly promotional (though also informative). Perhaps this wasn't the place where the cost of the scheme would be discussed.

Engaging with what you read

Critically rereading even this short quotation made me think about some of the issues that might arise but which were not necessarily explicitly stated. Perhaps there were some additional points that passed through your mind. It is often a good strategy to stop and look a little harder at some statements that you think might be important and try challenging some of the ideas put forward, or your own assumptions.

4.3 Scale of the NHS

Some indication of the scale of the NPfIT can be gained from the size of the NHS itself. I give below some statistics about the NHS from the *Chief Executive's Report to the NHS May 2005* (Department of Health, 2005). These statistics relate only to England, which, according to the most recent UK census in 2001, has a population of approximately 50 million (Office for National Statistics, 2001).

In 2004–5 there were:

305 million consultations with general practitioners or nurses in primary care.

13.5 million outpatient consultations.

Over 5.4 million people admitted to hospital for planned treatment.

686 million prescription items issued.

6.6 million phone calls made to NHS Direct.

9.3 million hits to the NHS Direct Online website.

Activity 26 (exploratory)

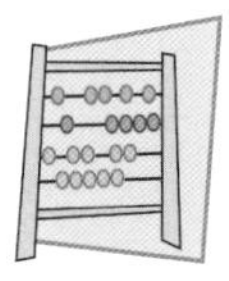

(a) According to the same NHS report, there were 31 500 general practitioners in England (to three significant figures). Taking the population as 50 million, how many potential patients was one general practitioner in England responsible for?

(b) Combine the calls made to NHS Direct with the number of 'hits' to the NHS Direct Online website. Calculate what these are as a percentage of the number of consultations with general practitioners or nurses in primary care.

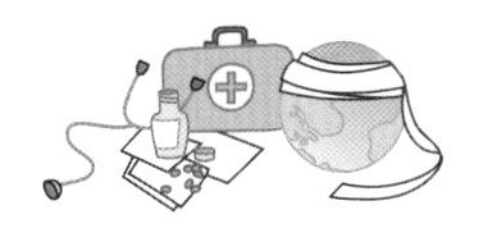

Comment

(a) Fifty million patients allocated to 31 500 general practitioners corresponds to an average allocation per general practitioner of:

$$\frac{50\,000\,000}{31\,500} \approx 1600$$

(Remember that the ≈ character means 'approximately equal to'. I have used it because I have rounded the answer to two significant figures.)

(b) The use of NHS Direct amounts to 6.6 million + 9.3 million instances. That is a total of 15.9 million instances. There were 305 million face-to-face consultations with primary health practitioners. Hence, telephone and online activity as a fraction of face-to-face consultation is:

$$\frac{15\,900\,000}{305\,000\,000} = 0.052 \text{ or } 5.2\% \text{ (to two significant figures)}$$

You can get the sense from even this brief examination of these statistics that the NHS is a large organisation and, significantly, some patients are making use of ICT as one means of accessing health information. It certainly seems timely, therefore, that ICT should increasingly be used within the NHS itself.

4.4 Components of the NPfIT

I mentioned earlier that creating a database of medical records (the Care Records service) was just one part of the NPfIT. The major parts of the NPfIT are as follows, starting with the Care Records Service. (The numbering is for later reference.)

1 Care Records Service. A database of clinical information on patients.

2 Contact. A centrally managed email and directory service provided free of charge to NHS organisations in England.

3 Choose and Book. A system by which general practitioners (GPs) and other primary care staff will be able to book initial hospital appointments electronically.

4 Electronic Transmission of Prescriptions. A system for sending prescriptions electronically to a pharmacist of the patient's choice.

5 New National Network. A national communication network (known as N3) linking general practitioners, hospitals, consultants and so on.

6 Picture Archiving and Communications Systems (PACS). These systems capture, store, distribute and display static or moving digital medical images.

7 Secondary Uses Service (SUS). The idea behind this service is to enable anonymous medical data to be made available to appropriate

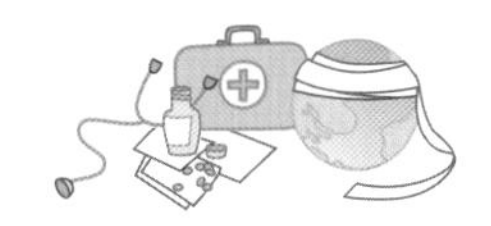

people for research, monitoring of medical performance, planning, public health campaigns, and so on.

8 National Library for Health (NLH). This is an electronic information resource, intended primarily for health workers.

9 GP2GP. A system for transferring medical records from one general practitioner to another. The most common use of this is likely to be when a person transfers to a different doctor, for instance following a change of address.

Activity 27 (exploratory)

Which of the NPfIT services listed above are mainly for accessing information and which are mainly for communication? You might decide that some are mixed, in which case you can classify them as mixed. (Some answers are debatable.)

Comment

Table 6 shows my answer. My first thought was that numbers 1, 3, 8 and 9 were information services. Then it occurred to me that remote access to this information was an essential part of the service, and this would require communication. I have not listed 7 as 'mixed', largely because I feel I do not know enough about it. However, I would not be surprised if this too depended on communications.

Table 6

	Service	Type of service
1	Care Records Service	Mixed
2	Contact	Communication
3	Choose and Book	Mixed
4	Electronic Transmission of Prescriptions	Communication
5	N3 network	Communication
6	PACS picture Archiving and Communications Systems	Mixed
7	SUS Secondary Uses Service	Information
8	NLH National Library for Health	Mixed
9	GP2GP	Mixed

Your answers to the last activity might not have agreed with mine, but I expect you found that communication was a vital part of the system. I shall therefore look at the NPfIT data communication network next.

4.5 The N3 communication network

One of the most important parts of the NPfIT project is the New National Network, or N3. Loosely speaking, this is the data network to link doctors, hospitals, consultants and all other sections of the health service in England and Scotland. (Wales and Scotland have had their own data network for some time before the NPfIT. The Scottish network will be linked to the N3 network.) It supersedes an earlier network, NHSnet.

Strictly speaking, the N3 is not a new physical network (in the sense of new wires and cables) but a system of agreements and contracts between the NHS and (ultimately) a range of broadband suppliers, to supply a broadband network for the NHS. The type of broadband service available is therefore wider ranging than that available to ordinary domestic consumers. The data rates available within the N3 range from 100 Mbps (envisaged for large hospitals) down to 2 Mbps for (typically) links to general practitioners' surgeries.

The N3, therefore, is effectively a system for buying a certain level of managed broadband support for the NHS. I will expand on what I mean by 'managed broadband support' after the following activity, but for now you can think of the N3 as a broadband network specially for all parts of the health service. (NHSnet was a similar type of network, but had a lower bandwidth and was less extensive.)

Activity 28 (exploratory)

Given that the N3 relates to broadband services within the NHS, why are any special arrangements necessary? Why shouldn't the NHS get its broadband services in just the same way as everyone else? (Hint: One reason has already been mentioned. If you cannot think of any other reasons, imagine your own medical details being transmitted over the internet.)

Comment

There are several reasons why the NHS's broadband provision is specially managed. I have picked out four.

Firstly, there is the question of bandwidth. As I have already mentioned, the kinds of bandwidth required go beyond what is offered to domestic consumers.

Secondly, there is the question of security. Where medical data is concerned, then there is naturally concern about the possibility of data being read by people who are not entitled to read it.

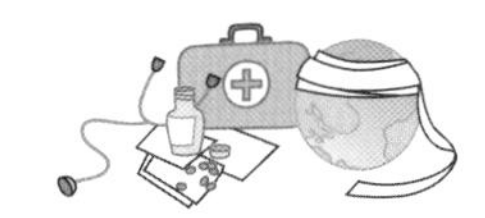

Thirdly, there is the question of availability. If you have broadband or a dial-up internet connection yourself, you will know that from time to time it is unavailable. The N3 contracts include stipulations about availability, which I will say more about below. Essentially the aim is to ensure that the network meets certain minimum standards of availability.

Fourthly, there is cost. By centralising its dealings with broadband suppliers, the NHS is likely to get services more cheaply than it would otherwise.

I mentioned that the N3 provides managed network support. It is managed in these senses:

- It offers a range of bandwidths for different parts of the network, as already mentioned.
- It guarantees a particular level of service, notably a particular level of 'availability'. I will expand on availability later.
- It is a virtual private network.

The last point, about virtual private networks, needs some elaboration, which I will do in the next section.

4.6 Virtual private networks

private network

To understand what a virtual private network is, let's first think what we mean by a **private network**. Many large organisations are geographically widespread. Think, for instance, of large chains of shops, supermarkets and banks. Very often each shop, supermarket or bank will have its own LAN. Typically a large organisation needs to join up its LANs for data communications.

If the only data that needed to be transmitted were emails, then using the internet might be a satisfactory way to do this. Usually, however, large organisations have more complex data requirements than that. For instance, they may have servers holding files that need to be accessed by people throughout the organisation, but which need to be inaccessible to people outside the organisation. Ideally, then, the organisation would have a private network, which is a data network for the exclusive use of the organisation, joining its LANs. Figure 15 shows, to the left, a private network for part of a health service.

Such a private network is separate from the internet. However, a large organisation would almost certainly need access to the internet from its own private network, so Figure 15 also shows a gateway to the internet. The gateway is, of course, a potential vulnerability as far as keeping the network private is concerned, but with good firewalls and other security the organisation's own network should be essentially private.

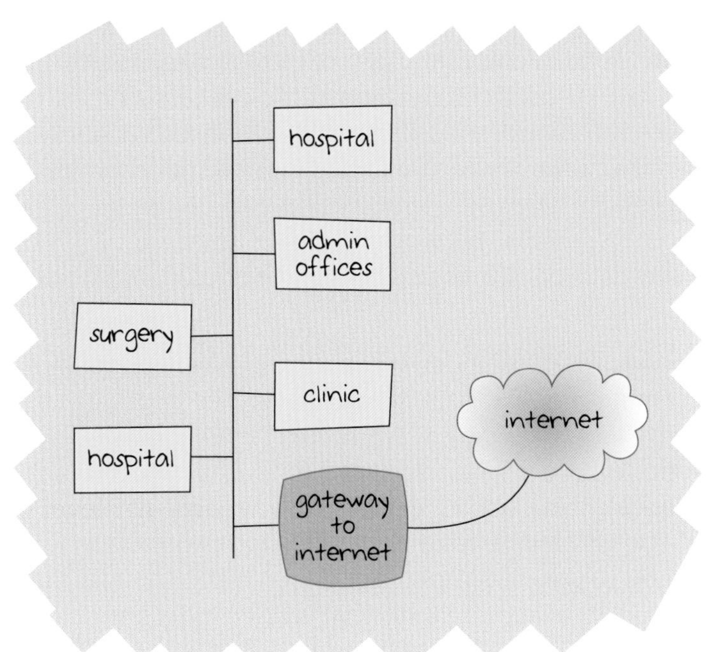

Figure 15 Private health-service network

Possible options for a private network with large geographical coverage could be:

- lay down cables or fibres between outlying parts of the organisation;
- lease lines from a telecommunications company to join outlying parts of the organisation;
- create wireless links (possibly using microwaves or satellite communications).

Any of these options is likely to be extremely expensive, and impractical for most organisations.

An alternative strategy is a **virtual private network (VPN)**, which uses a shared, or public, network for part of its data transmission and yet, to its users, appears to be private. Very often the internet forms part of the shared network.

virtual private network (VPN)

Several techniques exist for creating virtual private networks, and usually they involve the internet protocol (IP). For users of a VPN, the system is 'transparent'. That is, to the VPN's users the servers and networked computers within the organisation are easily accessible from their own computer, even though they might be in another part of the country, or even in a different country. Data traffic between the user's own computer and the remote server may pass, for part of the journey, over the internet. However, other internet users outside the VPN are not able to 'see' those servers from their computers. The network is therefore private, even though it uses shared data links.

The fact that VPN traffic passes over a shared network naturally raises concerns about security. Where confidentiality of data is particularly essential, **encryption** can be used. Encryption is the process of scrambling text to make it incomprehensible to unauthorised recipients. Authorised recipients have a 'key' which enables them to decrypt the text back to its original form. The use of encryption can be made transparent within the VPN, so that network users are unaware of it, but anyone intercepting the data on the shared network should not be able to read it.

encryption

Even with encryption you might wonder whether a VPN would really be secure enough for carrying medical data, for instance. The alternatives, though, might not be as secure as they seem at first sight. Consider a 'real' private network. If a piece of cable is known to be carrying only medical data (for instance), then would-be snoopers will know where to direct their attention. If a wireless private network were used, then eavesdropping would be relatively simple. But with a VPN, the fact that data goes along shared links makes it somewhat harder to isolate particular types of data, such as medical data, although it is conceivable that data from particular sources could be monitored.

Perhaps, though, when thinking about the security of confidential medical data, we should be as concerned about who has access to the data as about how the data is transmitted. This issue of access is a matter of **authentication**: users need to demonstrate that they are entitled to use the network, and the data to which it provides access. Passwords are an example of authentication. I will return to the issue of access to data in Section 4.8.

authentication

Activity 29 (exploratory)

The cost of creating a wired 'real' private network by installing new cables would be closely related to the distance covered by the network. Would the same necessarily be true of a VPN? Give a reason for your answer.

Comment

The cost of creating a VPN should be largely independent of the geographical size of the network. This is because it would share data links that already exist.

4.7 Availability

Activity 28 in Section 4.5 raised the question of availability of a network. Availability is simply the proportion of time, on average, for which a system is available for use. As the NPfIT involves putting so much data

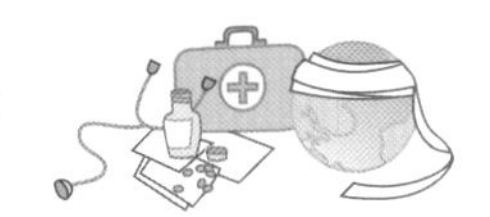

into computerised services, any one of which is liable to be occasionally unavailable, the issue of availability is naturally of considerable importance.

Suppose that, on average, in a period of 100 hours a system is available for 99.2 hours. Then we say that the availability is 99.2%. I say 'on average' because there may be many 100-hour periods during which the system remains available all the time; but there will be others during which the system is available for less than 99.2 hours.

An availability of 99.2% means that on average the system will be unavailable for 0.8 hours in every 100 hours, which amounts to 48 minutes. That unavailability need not be continuous. It might consist of several shorter periods of unavailability punctuating the periods when the system is available. An availability of 100% would mean that the system was always available.

Availability is closely related to the concept of probability. The box 'Availability and probability' looks at the connection between them.

Availability and probability

An availability of 90% means that the probability of the system working at any randomly chosen time is 0.9. An unavailability of 10% (which is the same as saying an availability of 90%) means that the probability of the system not working is 0.1.

In other words, availability is a way of expressing, as a percentage, the probability of a system working at any given time; and unavailability is a way of expressing the probability of it not working at any given time.

The principles for combining probabilities also apply to availabilities. For example, if a system consists of two independent components which both need to be working, the availability of the system can be found by multiplying the availabilities of the two components.

For example, if the components have separate availabilities of 60% and 70%, the combined availability of the system is:

$$\frac{60}{100} \times \frac{70}{100} = \frac{4200}{10000} = \frac{42}{100} = 42\%$$

In effect, we have calculated the probability of **both** components being operational at the same time. The corresponding probability calculation is:

$$0.6 \times 0.7 = 0.42$$

Expressed as a percentage this is 42%.

It is impossible to create a system with 100% availability, because it is impossible to create a system that never 'crashes' or that requires no maintenance or updating. Naturally the shorter the length of time for which any system is unavailable, the better. What can be done to improve availability? I will use an example relating to my commuting arrangements to explore this question.

I use a car to commute and I expect to be able to reach my workplace on nearly all the occasions that I set out. If my car has an availability of 98%, this could mean that the car is unavailable to me for a total of about a week in each year (2% of 52 weeks is just over a week). This could be quite a problem.

One strategy to improve availability, if there is no alternative such as public transport, would be to have a second car as a standby. Even if the availability of the standby car wasn't as good as that of the main car, the availability of transport would be high, provided each car has a reasonably high individual availability. In this case, I have access to transport if *either* car is available.

unavailability

I'll now make these ideas a little more concrete. What I want to find out is the length of time each year for which I will be without transport. The easiest way to do this is to calculate the **unavailability** of my transport. This is the probability that, at any given time, *both* cars are unavailable.

My main car, with an availability of 98%, is unavailable for 2% of the time on average. Suppose my backup car has an availability of 97%. My backup is unavailable for 3% of the time on average.

The unavailability of transport can be found by multiplying together the two individual values for unavailability:

$$\frac{2}{100} \times \frac{3}{100} = \frac{6}{10000} = \frac{0.06}{100} = 0.06\%$$

This is equivalent to multiplying together the individual probabilities of each car being unavailable at any given time.

The calculation shows that, on average, I will be without transport for only 0.06% of the year, which is 0.219 days, or approximately 5 hours and 15 minutes. So having a standby car is considerable better than having only one car.

Most critical services have standby arrangements; for example, hospitals have emergency electricity generators. Should the mains electricity supply fail, then critical procedures can carry on uninterrupted and the overall availability is therefore improved. For similar reasons, the Care Records Service database is duplicated and, in the event of a crash, the backup system will be used.

Activity 30 (self-assessment)

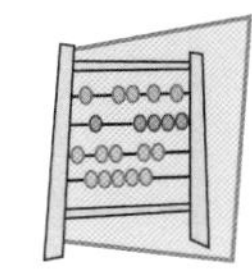

Earlier I calculated that a system with an availability of 99.2% would be unavailable for, on average, 48 minutes in every 100 hours. Suppose a backup system with an availability of 99.0% is used. (Assume the backup system comes into operation immediately if the main system fails.). For how long in a 100-hour period is no system available, on average?

Comment

The answer is at the end of this part.

What availability should the planners of the NPfIT aim for? 100% availability is impossible, and getting close to 100% is expensive. (In the case of my commuting, it means having a second car which is idle for most of the time.) This is one of those areas where there has to be a trade-off between costs and benefits. The appropriate trade-off is a matter of judgement. Table 7 shows the target availabilities for three separate parts of the NHS system, as quoted in 2005.

Table 7 Target availabilities for the components of the NPfIT

Service	Target availability
NHS Care Records: spine	99.8%
N3	99.2%
Choose and Book	99.5%

Source: NHS Connecting for Health (2005)

I indicated earlier that an availability of 99.2% corresponded to an average unavailability of 48 minutes in any 100 hours. You can see that this figure corresponds to the availability of the N3 network.

Suppose that a GP needed access to the spine of the NHS Care Records from the surgery. The GP would access those records over the network and would be dependent on the simultaneous availability of both the N3 network and the Care Records Service, which are independent systems. The simultaneous availability of the two systems is calculated by multiplying their separate availabilities.

From Table 7, the target availability of the network is 99.2% and the target availability of the spine of the Care Records system is 99.8%. The availability of both systems together is therefore:

$$\frac{99.2}{100} \times \frac{99.8}{100} = \frac{9900.16}{10000} = \frac{99.0016}{100} = 99.0016\%$$

Rounding the answer to three significant figures, we get a simultaneous availability of 99.0%. This is not an especially high value for availability, given the importance of a doctor having access to a patient's medical records.

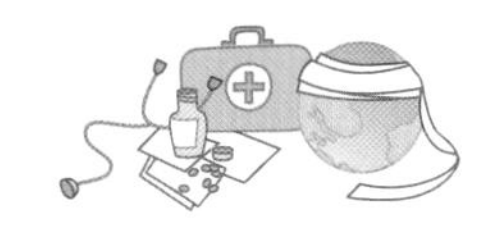

Activity 31 (self-assessment)

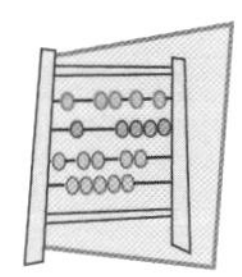

What is the availability of the Choose and Book accessed via the N3 network (assuming them to be independent systems)? Give your answer to three significant figures.

Comment

The answer is at the end of this part.

4.8 Confidentiality

I raised the question of confidentiality in connection with the N3 network. Many people within the NHS itself are concerned about the security implications of concentrating medical records in one system, where a large number of people might have access to them. The following extract from a newspaper article indicates the nature of their concern:

> Government plans to put the medical records of 50 million patients in England on a national electronic database pose even more of a threat to civil liberties than the ID card scheme, doctors' leaders warned yesterday.
>
> The patient care record – part of a £6.2bn programme to develop IT for the NHS – would allow GPs, hospitals and paramedics to access medical information that could save lives.
>
> But the British Medical Association (BMA) conference in Manchester was told it might also permit the leaking of intimate details about patients and their families divulged over many years in confidential consultations with GPs and consultants.
>
> Eleanor Scott, a GP from Barnet in north London, said: 'The information contained in this record will exceed anything on the national ID card.'
>
> A doctor's notes could include enough information to build up a full picture of a patient's social, sexual, religious and occupational history. 'No other database would contain that amount of information under one umbrella. Giving a government department access to that would be horrendous.'
>
> 'With over 50m records being copied on to the spine [...], and over 1m users [among NHS staff], the risks of errors, unauthorised access, identity theft and malicious tampering are legion,' Dr Scott added.
>
> Carvel (2005)

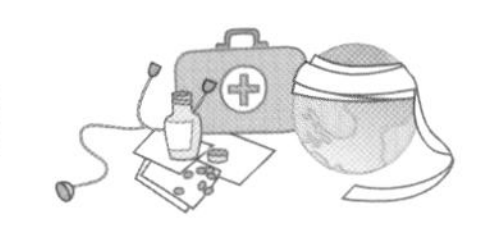

Activity 32 (exploratory)

In the extract above, what particular features of the NPfIT are singled out as potentially jeopardising confidentiality?

Comment

Firstly there is the concentration of a large amount of information in one system: 'No other database would contain that amount of information under one umbrella.'

Secondly there is the question of who has access to this information: 'Giving a government department access to that ...' and 'With over 1m users ...'.

Paper-based records may be old-fashioned and, in some respects, inefficient, but if they are kept under lock and key in a local surgery's filing cabinet there is clearly a limit on who can access them. When the same information is on a national database, the information could be almost anywhere, and access to the information might be much harder to regulate. Password control can be used for sensitive information, but sometimes leaks of sensitive information are due to a breach of trust, for example by a disgruntled employee, rather than an outside hacker. Accidental disclosure of information can also occur.

The General Medical Council guides the medical profession on the ethics of good medical practice and an extract from its guidance notes follows:

> 18. You must treat information about patients as confidential. If in exceptional circumstances there are good reasons why you should pass on information without a patient's consent, or against a patient's wishes, you must follow our guidance *Confidentiality: Protecting and Providing Information* and be prepared to justify your decision to the patient, if appropriate, and to the GMC and the courts, if called on to do so.
>
> General Medical Council (2001)

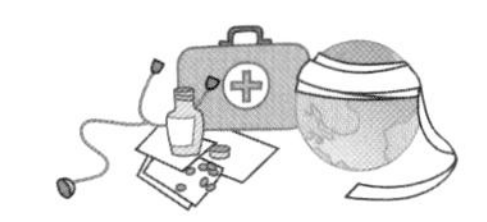

This is reassuring, but is it now outdated? Professor Ross Anderson of Cambridge University, UK, is a leading authority on information security. His home page contains the following:

> The Health and Social Care (Community Health and Standards) Act allowed the Government access to all medical records in the UK, for the purposes of 'Health Improvement'. It removed many of the patient privacy safeguards in previous legislation. In addition the new contract offered to GPs since 2003 moves ownership of family doctor computers to Primary Care Trusts.
>
> Anderson (n.d.)

At the time of writing there was a lively debate on this matter and this may well rumble on during your period of study. While you may trust a present government that introduces measures for the best of reasons, governments can change and then use existing measures for different purposes. Restoring hard-fought-for 'rights' may be more difficult in these circumstances.

4.9 Summary of Section 4

In this section I have provided a snapshot of the changes that are being introduced in just one large health service in Europe. The NPfIT in the NHS is built around the concept of an electronic patient record being held on a database within a Care Records Service. It also includes facilities such as electronic booking of hospital beds and electronic prescriptions.

Access to these facilities throughout the NHS depends on the provision of modern networks which allow information to be distributed to wherever it is needed. It is important that the new systems are available for as much of the time as possible, within the limitations of cost. I have demonstrated how the overall availability of systems can be calculated in simple cases.

Although these systems are intended to be more efficient and convenient for both patients and medical staff, there are ethical concerns following from the accessibility of medical information by many people within the health system, and the potential for external interference.

Summary of Block 4 Part 1

I have highlighted three areas of health where information and communication technologies are having a major effect.

In 'Accessing health information' the focus was on individuals' access to health-related information by means of ICT systems. I showed that the level of access differs depending on the ICT system being used and which part of the world people live in. I went on to look at the use that can be made of the information acquired, and this led to a discussion of probability and of decision trees.

In 'Telemedicine' I looked at the idea of medicine at a distance. Key developments here were remote consultation and remote surgery. We saw several possibilities, all of which are dependent on the bandwidth or reliability (or both) of the data communication link.

In 'Networking health' I gave an overview of the changes being introduced into just one example of a large national health service. The implications for medical staff, government and patients are very significant and there are many unresolved issues relating to confidentiality and access to medical records.

Answers to self-assessment activities

Activity 8

Here is the completed passage.

The two ideas that are exploited to pack in the digital channels are compression and flexible use of the transmission capacity (you could alternatively have said 'dynamic capacity allocation' for this second idea).

In dynamic capacity allocation (you could also have said 'flexible use of the transmission capacity') the available bandwidth (you could alternatively have said 'bit rate') is not necessarily allocated equally among all the channels. Instead, a channel with, say, a fast-changing picture will be allocated a higher proportion of the available bandwidth (or bit rate) than one with a picture that is changing more slowly.

Activity 9

(a) For all four countries, the number of internet users is lower than the number of telephone lines/cellular subscribers.

The most striking difference is that for Bangladesh, China and Uganda, the number of telephone lines/cellular subscribers is roughly 10 times as great as the number of internet users, whereas for Denmark the ratio is much lower – closer to 3.

(b) In Bangladesh, the rates of growth of telephone lines/cellular subscribers per 100 inhabitants and of internet users per 100 inhabitants are similar.

In China, the rate of growth of internet use is much higher than the rate of growth of telephone lines/cellular subscribers, though the latter is still growing markedly.

In Denmark also there are signs of some continuing growth, more so than in the case of telephone subscribers. However, the growth appears small compared with that of China.

The data for Uganda tells a different story: here the rate of growth of internet use is slower than the rate of growth of telephone lines/cellular subscribers.

Activity 13

(a) It could be argued that using a telephone to phone NHS Direct has elements of both information push and information pull. The two-way nature of the interaction and the fact that the user initiates the process could make it more strongly information pull, but the user is not likely to be presented with a wide range of resources or options to select from. After the initial description of the symptoms by the user, the nurse is likely to take the lead and suggest a cause of the

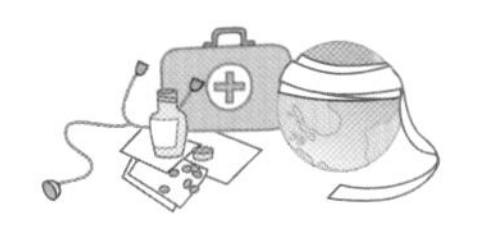

problem and what action to take next. This would be closer to information push. I think that different users could experience different balances of the two elements.

(b) Broadcast radio is a one-way broadcast system that is strongly information push in character, though choosing the station to listen to is a limited form of information pull. However, sometimes listeners are given the opportunity to phone in (or text or email), perhaps asking questions which a speaker may be expected to respond to. Listener interactivity of this sort could provide a degree of information pull but would involve the use of additional ICTs.

(c) In this context, the Web can be thought of as something like an online library, so this ICT system is characterised more strongly as information pull. However, there are often accompanying elements of 'push' – for example in advertisements that can be difficult to avoid.

(d) NHS Direct Interactive accessed through digital television would also fit closely with the information-pull model, with the same qualification as in part (c).

Activity 15

(a) There is one red pen in a drawer of eight pens. So the probability of getting a red pen is 1 divided by 8, which is 0.125.

(b) There are four black pens in a drawer of eight pens. So the probability of getting a black pen is 4 divided by 8, which is 0.5.

Activity 16

(a) The probability of getting a blue pen is 0.375, as I showed in the text just before Activity 15. The probability of getting a black pen is 0.5, as you calculated in Activity 15. The probability of getting either of these colours is the sum of the two probabilities. So the probability is $0.375 + 0.5 = 0.875$.

(As an alternative: there are 7 pens that are either black or blue, so the probability of getting a black or blue pen should be 7 divided by 8, and this is indeed 0.875.)

(b)

(i) The probability of throwing a 2 is 0.167 (to three significant figures), as you saw at various points in the text.

(ii) The probability of drawing one particular card from a heap of 15 cards is 1/15 or 0.0667 (to three significant figures).

(iii) The probability of getting bonus points is the probability of throwing a 2 and then getting one particular card. It is found by multiplying the probabilities of parts (i) and (ii) together, so it is $0.167 \times 0.0667 = 0.0111$ (again to three significant figures).

This is about 1 in 100, so your chances are not very high!

(c) Here the probability of your losing the points and the probability of your not losing the points must add to 1 because the two events are mutually exclusive (there is no other possible outcome). So the probability that you don't lose the large number of points is $1 - 0.02 = 0.98$.

This is reassuringly high.

Activity 17

Table 8 shows the most likely entries in your table, but you may have found other valid points.

Table 8 Differences between access in developing and developed countries

	A difference between access in developing countries and access in developed countries
Telephones	Developed countries have a well-developed PSTN infrastructure which uses interconnecting cables; developing countries are more likely to use cellular technology for some portions of the infrastructure. or There is more likelihood of shared use of telephones in developing countries. (This point is not made explicitly, but can be deduced.)
Broadcast radio	Because of lack of mains electricity in rural areas in many developing countries there is a need for devices such as wind-up radios.
The internet	There are much higher numbers of internet users per 100 inhabitants in developed countries than there are in developing countries.

Activity 21

The round-trip propagation delay is the time for the signal to travel there and back. It is given by the expression:

$$\text{time taken} = \frac{\text{distance}}{\text{speed}}$$

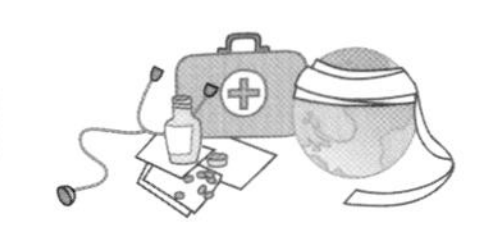

As the total distance is 10 000 km or 10×10^6 m, and the speed of propagation is 2×10^8 m/s, we have:

$$\begin{aligned} \text{time taken} &= \frac{10 \times 10^6}{2 \times 10^8}\ \text{s} \\ &= \frac{10\ 000\ 000}{200\ 000\ 000}\ \text{s} \\ &= \frac{1}{20}\ \text{s} \\ &= 50\ \text{ms} \end{aligned}$$

This time delay is comparable in magnitude with the video processing time of 70 ms.

The relative proportions are:

propagation time:

$$\frac{50}{155} = 0.322 \text{ or approximately } 32\%$$

video processing:

$$\frac{70}{155} = 0.452 \text{ or approximately } 45\%$$

Activity 24

The total size of the image files to be transmitted is

$$280\ \text{KB} + 980\ \text{KB} + 420\ \text{KB} + 730\ \text{KB} = 2410\ \text{KB}$$

and

$$1\ \text{KB} = 1024 \times 8\ \text{bits}$$

The transmission time is therefore:

$$\frac{2410 \times 1024 \times 8}{128 \times 10^3}\ \text{s}$$

which works out to 154 s (to three significant figures).

154 seconds is just over two and a half minutes. So the delay would be about two and a half minutes. Whether this is acceptable depends very much on the context. If the images were being sent remotely for an expert opinion during an emergency operation, this transmission time might well be unacceptable. But for many other applications of the type described earlier in this section, it would be perfectly adequate.

Activity 25

Here are the applications you are most likely to have mentioned.

(a) The only example that is definitely stated to operate using only a standard telephone line is the basic form of the CareCompanion described in Section 3.2. It may also be possible to implement the cystic fibrosis example (Activity 20) and to send the X-ray and other images in the Bhuj example (Section 3.2) over a normal telephone line.

(b) The transatlantic gall bladder operation (Section 3.3) used a 10 Mbps link. Although it is not stated directly, a rate of over 5 Mbps would also probably be needed for the Guam heart-surgery example in my comments on Activity 20 (high-resolution video was used). Trauma Pod, too, will almost certainly need high-bit-rate (wireless) links.

Activity 30

The unavailabilities of the two systems separately are 0.8% and 1%. The fraction of time for which there is no working system is therefore:

$$\frac{0.8}{100} \times \frac{1}{100} = \frac{0.8}{10000} = \frac{0.008}{100} = 0.008\%$$

On average, in a 100-hour period, there is no working system for:

$$\frac{0.008}{100} \times 100 \text{ hours} = 0.008 \text{ hours}$$

0.008 hours is 28.8 seconds.

Activity 31

The availability of N3 is 99.2 % and the availability of Choose and Book by itself is 99.5%. The availability of Choose and Book via the N3 network is therefore:

$$\frac{99.2}{100} \times \frac{99.5}{100} = \frac{9870.4}{10000} = \frac{98.704}{100} = 98.704\%$$

To three significant figures, this is 98.7%. Again this is not an especially high value, but in this case the availability of the system is not so vital. The booking could always be made later.

References

Anderson, R. (n.d.) *Security of Medical Information Systems*, [online] http://www.cl.cam.ac.uk/users/rja14 [Accessed 21 July 2005]

Balancing Act (2005) 'Power in the palm of your hand – Freeplay to launch self-powered mobile charger in Africa', (May) [online] http://www.balancingact-africa.com/news/back/balancing-act_257.html, vol. 257, no. 20 [Accessed 11 July 2005]

Borland, J. and Hu, J. (2004) 'Broadband: A life-saving technology', 27 July [online] at http://news.zdnet.com/2100-9584_22-5284954.html [Accessed 21 July 2005]

Brewer, E. et al. (2005) 'The Case for Technology in Developing Regions', *Computer*, vol. 38, no. 6, June, p. 27.

Carvel, J. (2005) 'Security Fears Over Medical Database', *Guardian*, 30 June, p. 7.

Cross, M. (2004) 'In sickness or in health?', *IEE Review*, October 2004, pp. 38–41.

Department of Health (2005) *Chief Executive's Report to the NHS May 2005: Statistical Supplement*, Department of Health Publications, May 2005. Available online at http://www.dh.gov.uk/assetRoot/04/11/04/16/04110416.pdf.

The Economist (2005) 'Behind the digital divide', vol. 374 no. 8417, pp. 21–22 of *Technology Quarterly* section.

Elliott, J. (2003) 'NHS Stories: Telemedicine', 12 September [online] http://news.bbc.co.uk/1/hi/health/3080564.stm [Accessed 21 July 2005]

England, A. (2005) 'Africa calling', *FT Magazine*, 12 November, pp. 35–37.

European Commission (2004) *e-Health - making healthcare better for European citizens: An action plan for a European e-Health Area*, Commission of the European Communities, Brussels, 2004. Available online at www.epha.org/IMG/pdf/e-health_action_plan.pdf

General Medical Council (2001) *Good Medical Practice: Duties and Responsibilities of Doctors*, General Medical Council, London. Available online at http://www.gmc-uk.org/standards/GMP.pdf

Harris, G (2002), 'India: telemedicine's great new frontier', *IEEE Spectrum*, vol. 39, no. 4, April, pp. 16–17.

Haviland, C (2003) 'Healing hearts by remote control', 14 August [online] http://news.bbc.co.uk/1/hi/world/south_asia/3148509.stm [Accessed 21 July 2005]

Home Telehealth Ltd (2004) 'Porter Hills Services Adds New Telehealth Monitoring for Seniors in West Michigan' [online] http://www.hometelehealthltd. co.uk/home.htm [Accessed 18 July 2005]

Moore, S. K. (2002) 'Extending healthcare's reach', *IEEE Spectrum*, vol. 39, no. 1, January, pp. 66–71.

NASA (2004) 'NASA-funded telemedicine research brings medical care to people living in Earth's remote regions, improves space medicine', 5 May [online] http://www.nasa.gov/centers/marshall/news/news/releases/2004/04-129.html [Accessed 21 July 2005]

NHS (2005) 'National Programme for IT in the NHS' [online] http://www.connectingforhealth.nhs.uk [Accessed 7 July 2005]

NHS Connecting for Health (2005) 'Service summary 3 July', 5 July [online] http://www.connectingforhealth.nhs.uk/delivery/servicemanagement/statistics/operational [Accessed 10 July 2005]

Office for National Statistics (2001) [online] www.statistics.gov.uk/census2001/census2001.asp [Accessed 13 July 2005]

PhysOrg (2005) 'Trauma Pod Robot to Save Soldiers' Lives on the Battlefield' [online] http://www.physorg.com/news3544.html [Accessed 18 July 2005]

United Nations (2000) 'UN Millennium Development Goals' [online] http://www.un.org/millenniumgoals/ [Accessed 11 July 2005]

Wireless Healthcare (2005) 'ESA Aids ASIA' [online] http://www.wirelesshealthcare.co.uk/wh/news/wk04-0004.htm [Accessed 21 July 2005]

World Health Organization (1946) *Preamble to the Constitution of the World Health Organization* as adopted by the International Health Conference [online], New York, 19–22 June, 1946; signed on 22 July 1946 by the representatives of 61 States (Official Records of the World Health Organization, no. 2, p. 100) and entered into force on 7 April 1948, http://www.who.int/about/definition/en/ [Accessed 11 July 2005]

Acknowledgements

Grateful acknowledgement is made to the following sources for permission to reproduce material within this book.

Text

Harris G., (2004), 'India Telemedicine's Great New Frontier', *IEEE Spectrum*

'Behind the Digital Divide', © The Economist Newspaper Limited, London (12th March 2005)

Figures

Figure 3: © Science Museum

Figure 6: 'Worldspace Global Satellite Coverage Area', © Worldspace

Figure 7: AMI ASR-WS201 © Worldspace

Figure 9: Copyright © 2004–2005 Informitv and Contributors

Figure 13: Photographs courtesy of Home Telehealth Limited

Figure 14: 'The Zeus System', Motion Incorporated

Appendix

Behind The Digital Divide

Development: Much is made of the 'digital divide' between rich and poor. What do people on the ground think about it?

December 3, 2005

The Economist

IN THE village of Embalam in southern India, about 15 miles outside the town of Pondicherry, Arumugam and his wife, Thillan, sit on the red earth in front of their thatch hut. She is 50 years old; he is not sure, but thinks he is around 75. Arumugam is unemployed. He used to work as a drum-beater at funerals, but then he was injured, and now he has trouble walking. Thillan makes a little money as a part-time agricultural labourer – about 30 rupees ($0.70) a day, ten days a month. Other than that, they get by on meagre (and sporadic) government disability payments.

In the new India of cybercafés and software tycoons, Arumugam and Thillan, and the millions of other villagers around the country like them, seem like anachronisms. But just a few steps outside their section of the village – a section known as the 'colony', where the untouchables traditionally live – the sheen of India's technology boom is more evident in a green room equipped with five computers, state-of-the-art solar cells and a wireless connection to the internet. This is the village's Knowledge Centre, one of 12 in the region set up by a local non-profit organisation, the M. S. Swaminathan Research Foundation (MSSRF). The centres, established with the aid of international donor agencies and local government support, offer villagers a range of information, including market prices for crops, job listings, details of government welfare schemes, and health advice.

A conservative estimate of the cost of the equipment in the Embalam centre is 200,000 rupees ($4,500), or around 55 years' earnings for Thillan. Annual running costs are extra. When asked about the centre, Thillan laughs. 'I don't know anything about that,' she says. 'It has no connection to my life. We're just sitting here in our house trying to survive.'

Scenes like these, played out around the developing world, have led to something of a backlash against rural deployments of new information and communications technologies, or ICTs, as they are known in the jargon of development experts. In the 1990s, at the height of the technology boom, rural ICTs were heralded as catalysts for 'leapfrog development', 'information societies' and a host of other digital-age panaceas for poverty. Now they have largely fallen out of favour: none other than Bill Gates, the chairman of Microsoft, derides them as distractions from the real problems of

development. 'Do people have a clear view of what it means to live on $1 a day?' he asked at a conference on the digital divide in 2000. 'About 99% of the benefits of having a PC come when you've provided reasonable health and literacy to the person who's going to sit down and use it.' That is why, even though Mr Gates made his fortune from computers, the Bill & Melinda Gates Foundation, now the richest charity in the world, concentrates on improving health in poor countries.

The backlash against ICTs is understandable. Set alongside the medieval living conditions in much of the developing world, it seems foolhardy to throw money at fancy computers and internet links. Far better, it would appear, to spend scarce resources on combating AIDS, say, or on better sanitation facilities. Indeed, this was the conclusion reached by the recently concluded Copenhagen Consensus project, which brought together a group of leading economists to prioritise how the world's development resources should be spent. The panel came up with 17 priorities: spending more on ICTs was not even on the list.

Still, it may be somewhat hasty to write off rural technology altogether. Charles Kenny, a senior economist at the World Bank who has studied the role of ICTs in development, says that traditional cost-benefit calculations are in the best of cases 'an art, not a science'. With ICTs, he adds, the picture is further muddied by the newness of the technologies; economists simply do not know how to quantify the benefits of the internet.

The view from the ground

Given the paucity of data, then, and even of sound methodologies for collecting the data, an alternative way to evaluate the role of ICTs in development is simply to ask rural residents what they think. Applied in rural India, in the villages served by the MSSRF, this approach reveals a more nuanced picture than that suggested by the sceptics, though not an entirely contradictory one.

Villagers like Arumugam and Thillan – older, illiterate and lower caste – appear to have little enthusiasm for technology. Indeed, Thillan, who lives barely a five-minute walk from the village's Knowledge Centre, says she did not even know about its existence until two months ago (even though the centre has been open for several years). When Thillan and a group of eight neighbours are asked for their development priorities – a common man's version of the Copenhagen Consensus – they list sanitation, land, health, education, transport, jobs – the list goes on and on, but it does not include computers, or even telephones. They are not so much sceptical of ICTs as oblivious; ICTs are irrelevant to their lives. This attitude is echoed by many villagers at the bottom of the social and economic ladder. In the fishing community of Veerapatinam, the site of another MSSRF centre, Thuradi, aged 45, sits on the beach sorting through his catch. 'I'm illiterate,' he says, when asked about the centre. 'I don't know how to use a computer, and I have to fish all day.'

But surely technology can provide information for the likes of Thuradi, even if he does not sit down in front of the computers himself? Among other things, the centre in this village offers information on wave heights and weather patterns (information that Thuradi says is already available on television). Some years ago, the centre also used satellites to map the movements of large schools of fish in the ocean. But according to another fisherman, this only benefited the rich: poor fishermen, lacking motorboats and navigation equipment, could not travel far enough, or determine their location precisely enough, to use the maps.

Such stories bring to mind the uneven results of earlier technology-led development efforts. Development experts are familiar with the notion of 'rusting tractors' – a semi-apocryphal reference to imported agricultural technologies that littered poor countries in the 1960s and 1970s. Mr Kenny says he similarly anticipates 'a fair number of dusty rooms with old computers piled up in them around the countryside.'

That may well be true, but it does not mean that the money being channelled to rural technology is going entirely unappreciated. Rural ICTs appear particularly useful to the literate, to the wealthier and to the younger – those, in other words, who sit at the top of the socio-economic hierarchy. In the 12 villages surrounding Pondicherry, students are among the most frequent users of the Knowledge Centres; they look up exam results, learn computer skills and look for jobs. Farmers who own land or cattle, and who are therefore relatively well-off, get veterinary information and data on crop prices.

Outside the Embalam colony, at a village teashop up the road from the temple, Kumar, the 35-year-old shop owner, speaks glowingly about the centre's role in disseminating crop prices and information on government welfare schemes, and says the Knowledge Centre has made his village 'famous'. He cites the dignitaries from development organisations and governments who have visited; he also points to the fact that people from 25 surrounding villages come to use the centre, transforming Embalam into something of a local information hub.

At the centre itself, Kasthuri, a female volunteer who helps run the place, says that the status of women in Embalam has improved as a result of using the computers. 'Before, we were just sitting at home,' she says. 'Now we feel empowered and more in control.' Some economists might dismiss such sentiments as woolly headed. But they are indicators of a sense of civic pride and social inclusiveness that less conventional economists might term human development or well-being.

A question of priorities

Given the mixed opinions on the ground, then, the real issue is not whether investing in ICTs can help development (it can, in some cases, and for some people), but whether the overall benefits of doing so outweigh those of investing in, say, education or health. Leonard Waverman of the London Business School has compared the impact on GDP of increases in teledensity

(the number of telephones per 100 people) and the primary-school completion rate. He found that an increase of 100 basis points in teledensity raised GDP by about twice as much as the same increase in primary-school completion. As Dr Waverman acknowledges, however, his calculations do not take into account the respective investment costs – and it is the cost of ICTs that makes people such as Mr Gates so sceptical of their applicability to the developing world.

Indeed, Ashok Jhunjhunwala, a professor at the Indian Institute of Technology in Chennai (formerly Madras), argues that cost is the 'deciding factor' in determining whether the digital divide will ever be bridged. To that end, Dr Jhunjhunwala and his colleagues are working on a number of low-cost devices, including a remote banking machine and a fixed wireless system that cuts the cost of access by more than half. But such innovation takes time and is itself expensive.

Perhaps a more immediate way of addressing the cost of technology is to rely on older, more proven means of delivering information. Radios, for example, are already being used by many development organisations; their cost (under $10) is a fraction of the investment (at least $800) required for a telephone line. In Embalam and Veerapatinam, few people actually ever sit at a computer; they receive much of their information from loudspeakers on top of the Knowledge Centre, or from a newsletter printed at the centre and delivered around the village. Such old-fashioned methods of communication can be connected to an internet hub located further upstream; these hybrid networks may well represent the future of technology in the developing world.

[...]

Part 2
Road transport

Roger Jones and Allan Jones

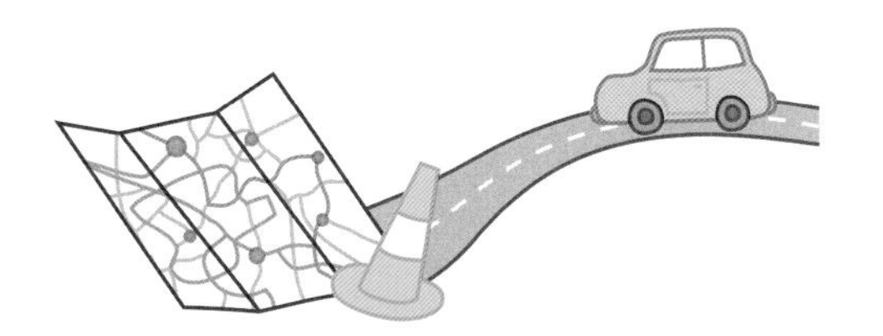

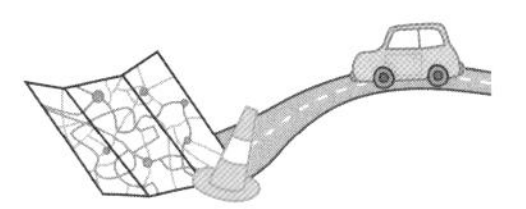

1 Networks and transport

1.1 Road traffic: the issues

In this part of Block 4 we shall be looking at some areas where ICTs can improve the use of the road network. We shall be looking at:

- similarities and differences between road and data networks;
- how drivers and traffic control centres can be informed of the state of the traffic on roads;
- the way traffic queues form;
- some ideas for controlling congestion by road charging;
- the ways in which data networks can be created between vehicles;
- some novel ideas for the use of ICTs in conjunction with road vehicles;
- some social and ethical factors relating to these developments in the use of ICTs.

Running throughout this material is the constant thread of network management: How do we get the information needed in order to manage a network (such as the road network), and how can we control the traffic on the network?

It is easy to appreciate why there is a great deal of interest in using ICTs to help manage road networks. Between 1971 and 2001, the number of cars on European roads trebled, and continued to grow at 3 million cars per year. Projecting forward to 2010, it was predicted that the demand for goods transportation would increase by 38%, and that for passengers by 24% (European Commission, 2001). Building new roads, or upgrading existing ones, does not provide a lasting solution because new road capacity often encourages increased road use – leading to further congestion and environmental problems. Congested transport networks are inefficient, and have adverse economic consequences when people and goods are delayed. Emergency services are also adversely affected.

One of the ways in which ICTs might be able to help with the problems outlined above is by enabling better utilisation of the road network. In other words, ICTs can, potentially, enable the road network to be better managed.

1.2 Different kinds of network

I now want you to take a step back and think about what the term 'network' really means so that you can consider what other types of network exist. You should then be able to compare the features and functions of different types of network.

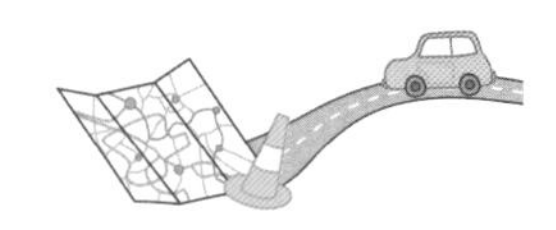

Activity 1 (exploratory)

Look for a definition of *network* on Google by typing *define: network* in the search window. From the responses look for the three or four key words that crop up repeatedly and make a note of these.

What other types of network are there, other than communication networks and road transport networks? Give two examples of these.

Comment

When I searched, I noticed that the terms *interconnectedness*, *resources* and *sharing* seemed to crop up frequently. I can relate these terms to communication networks where nodes are interconnected by communication links and the resources (such as data or hardware or the links themselves) are often shared by many users – computers, devices or people.

Other types of network were also suggested in the results of my search. For example, utilities such as water, gas and electricity are delivered via distribution networks. These networks are built from pipes or cables and suitable control equipment such as valves, switches and measurement instrumentation. The purpose of each of these forms of network is to convey the resources to where they are needed, such as homes and businesses.

I also found reference to networks in a human sense (for example, knowledge networks or 'old pals' networks) and sometimes the term is used as a verb such as 'to network within a certain professional area'. People can be regarded as resources, but in this case it's not that people themselves are distributed along pipes or cables, but it is their knowledge, expertise or talent that is 'networked' to where it is needed.

You should be able to appreciate from Activity 1 that networks provide the means to access and share some resources. Sometimes these resources are introduced into a network by a service provider; this could be an electricity or water company, for instance. In other networks (and here I am thinking of a road transport network) the network itself is the main resource whose use needs to be shared out between many users.

I'd like you to explore how a transport network fits some of these ideas. In particular, I would like you to consider the similarities and differences between transport networks and communication networks. Here I'm thinking of transport networks that include roads and railways. Busy air corridors or shipping lanes could also be thought of as links in transport networks, though the term 'network' isn't generally used in these cases.

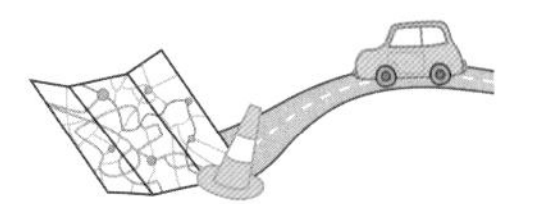

Activity 2 (exploratory)

Thinking about road and rail networks, what physical features of these networks can you associate with the network nodes, interconnecting links and the resources being shared? Also, what is physically being conveyed by these networks? Write some ideas in Table 1.

Table 1 Physical and network features of road and rail (blank for Activity 2)

Features	Rail network	Road network
Network nodes		
Interconnecting links		
Shared resources		
What is conveyed		

Comment

My ideas are summarised in Table 2, but I have also indicated my broader thinking in the paragraphs after the table.

Table 2 Physical and network features of road and rail

Features	Rail network	Road network
Network nodes	Railway stations as access nodes. Points as routing nodes.	Road junctions, roundabouts, motorway access points such as slip roads.
Interconnecting links	Rails.	Lanes, roads, motorways.
Shared resources	Passenger-carrying capacity of the rolling stock and the supporting systems.	Capacity of the roads to carry traffic and supporting systems.
What is conveyed	People and goods.	People and goods.

In railway networks, railway stations are important access nodes where passengers can board or leave a train. Between stations, 'points' can be thought of as routing nodes, directing trains towards their destination. The links between nodes are the rails themselves. The resources of the network include the access and routing nodes, the rolling stock (the trains, carriages and wagons) and the signalling

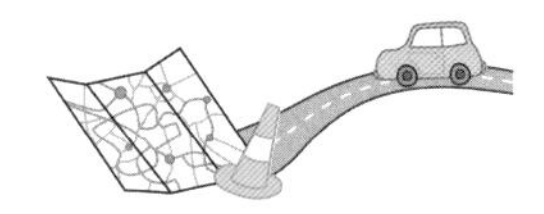

> systems that together support the ability to carry passengers and goods from one place to another.
>
> For road networks there is a hierarchy of motorway links, major trunk roads, urban roads and streets, country lanes and so on that in combination make up a single transport network. On motorways, we can think of nodes as being the main access points or motorway intersections. On trunk roads, there are road junctions (sometimes with roundabouts or traffic lights) that can be thought of as nodes.
>
> The network links are the roads themselves and the network resource is essentially the capacity of the road links to carry vehicles, but this needs to be shared out amongst the many users of a road network. A difference between rail and road networks is that in road networks the 'rolling stock' (cars and lorries) is not provided by the network.

If we think about how a transport network such as a national road network is to be managed, we need to think about what to include within the system we are managing. Figure 1 shows my view of the system that needs to be managed. You can see that I have included both the 'network' and the 'service user' within the system boundary. (There will, in general, be many service users.) In a railway transport system, the units in which people are being conveyed (the railway carriages) are usually owned by the service provider and the user is passive in terms of exercising any control with regard to direction, speed and departure times. In contrast, in road transport systems the units in which people or goods are being conveyed are, for the most part, private vehicles, with independent human individuals in charge of their functions. This presents a much greater possibility for conflicts of interest to arise both between different users of the road transport system and between users and what I have termed the service provider or the manager of those services.

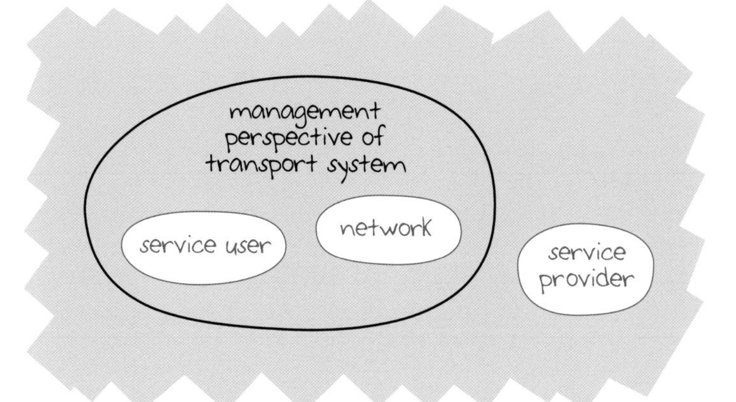

Figure 1 System map of a transport network

By including both the users and the network within the system, I am acknowledging that there could be two ways to manage the system. One way to manage the system is by managing the 'supply' side – the road network itself and its availability. Another way is to manage the

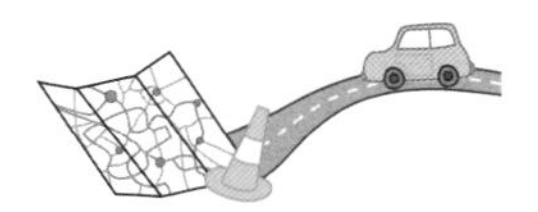

'demand' side – the users who want to use the network. For instance, one way to manage congestion in certain parts of the network might be to discourage people from using that part of the network. You will see some potential ways of doing this as you work through this part of Block 4. These two approaches to managing the system are not, of course, exclusive; managing both the supply and demand would be reasonable approaches.

1.3 Managing networks

All networks need to be managed. The roles of management in general can be summarised, very basically, as planning, monitoring, and controlling. Management can be carried out by humans or computer systems, and often both.

The role of planning in management is fairly obvious, because managers must plan for future requirements. However, it is the monitoring and controlling functions that I want to highlight in relation to the use of road networks. Monitoring and controlling may sound ominous (and can be, in the context of surveillance and coercion), but they are necessary management activities.

Monitoring means observing and, usually, measuring what is going on in a system. In a work situation, a manager will observe and collect information about what is happening in the various parts of the organisation for which the manager has responsibility. In a network too it is necessary to observe what is happening, with a view to identifying problems at an early stage.

Controlling, in the context of monitoring and controlling, is where a manager needs to make corrective action to resolve a problem. An example of this in a work situation could be where a vital process does not happen because someone is absent or because a piece of equipment is missing. The control action would be to put the appropriate resource in place, so that normal activity could resume. An example in a road network would be where road traffic is obstructed, and the control action would involve removing, or at least minimising the effect of, the obstruction. Controlling also has a wider sense, for example in terms of a manager controlling access to data, or controlling finances in a business; but these are not my main concern here.

The management of road networks is generally carried out at control centres covering the major regions of a country. An example of such a centre is shown in Figure 2. At these control centres, traffic in various parts of the system can be monitored via the many display screens. Images for these screens come from cameras installed at various critical points. Typically the monitors can be switched to show images from different cameras, and cameras can be remotely manipulated to capture different parts of the scene, or to zoom in and out. Control centres usually also have some limited means of controlling traffic, for example

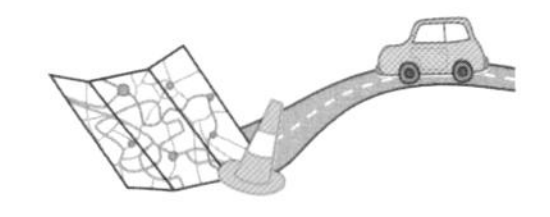

by overriding traffic lights, closing lanes, and using signs to warn drivers of problems. The management of the road network is therefore supported by a large communication network.

Figure 2 Traffic control centre

Activity 3 (self-assessment)

Monitoring and controlling a network relies on information about what is happening on a network being conveyed to a manager, and the manager's responses being conveyed back to the network. In Figure 3 I have indicated some possible directions of information flow over a communication network that is supporting the operation of a transport network. The arrows are labelled A, B, C, D. Identify the arrows which correspond to the primary flow of information in the following scenarios:

(a) A manager is automatically alerted to congestion on the road network.

(b) A driver slows down in response to an automatic sign warning of fog.

(c) A manager switches on a sign to close a lane.

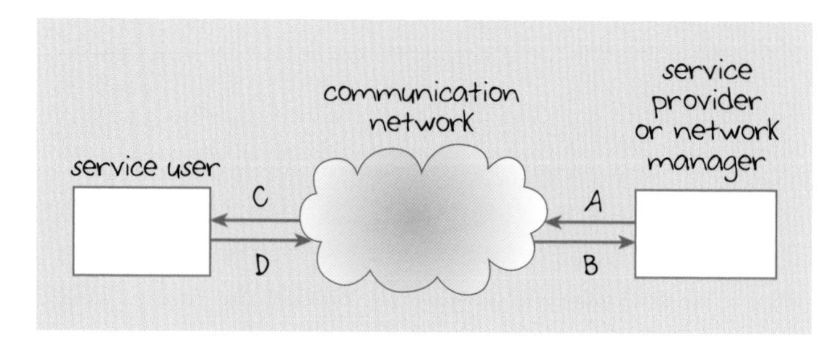

Figure 3 Information flow

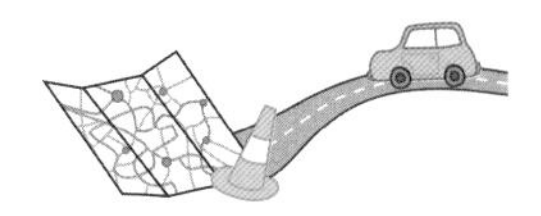

Comment

The answer is given at the end of this part.

1.4 Open and closed loops

In talking about the different directions of information flow, I find it helpful to use some of the language of control engineering.

open loop

In **open-loop** control there is no correcting mechanism if the output of the process drifts away from what it is supposed to be. For example, someone filling a bath might simply turn on both taps halfway and leave the bath to look after itself for five minutes. This might be satisfactory on most occasions, but on a day when the water pressure is higher or lower than normal, or when the hot water is not at its usual temperature, the result might be unsatisfactory.

closed loop

In **closed-loop** control the output of the process is monitored while it is happening, and corrective action taken if the output looks as though it is drifting away from what is required. With the bath, the person might check every minute that the bath is filling at the right rate and that the temperature is right. If either is going adrift, corrective action can be taken. Closed-loop control, therefore, depends on monitoring the output, and correcting the input in the light of what is happening at the output.

Ideas of open-loop and closed-loop control are relevant to the management of road transport systems because, as we have seen, traffic control embodies the idea of monitoring the network and taking some corrective actions (such as closing lanes, imposing temporary speed limits, and so on).

Activity 4 (self-assessment)

Which of the following involve open-loop control and which involve closed-loop control?

(a) Aiming and firing a single arrow at a target in archery.

(b) Steering a car round a bend.

(c) Cooking a soufflé, in which opening the opaque oven door to check progress can ruin the result.

(d) Cooking a casserole, in which experienced cooks test the dish from time to time and add more herbs, salt or pepper as necessary.

Comment

The answer is given at the end of this part.

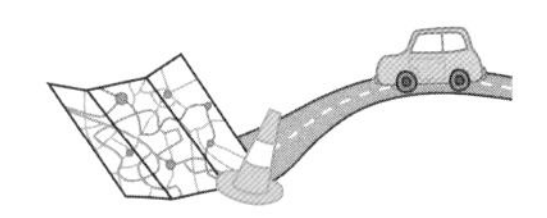

1.5 Summary of Section 1

Networks are ways of sharing a resource. In some cases, the network is used to distribute the resource. In other cases, such as roads, the network itself is the resource.

Network management is required if the network is to work properly. Network management depends on data about network use, obtained from monitoring the use of the network.

In open-loop control, once the process is under way there is no corrective action derived from the output. In closed-loop control, the output of the process is monitored as it happens, and the input modified to bring the output closer to what is required.

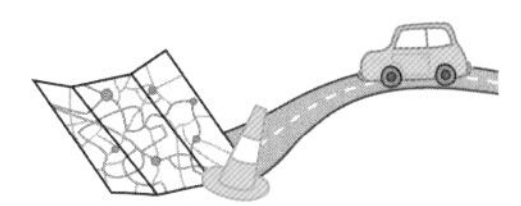

2 Traffic information

2.1 Traffic and congestion

Sometimes we accept words and terminology, assuming that we know their general meaning. But stopping to question our own understanding and carry out some further enquiry can help with learning about a topic. When a new word crops up, or a familiar word is used in a new context, it is useful to check the meaning by either doing a web search or looking in a dictionary. It strikes me that 'traffic' could be such a word.

I entered the term *define: traffic* into the Google search window to look for definitions of the word 'traffic'. This resulted in many responses, some of them clearly inappropriate, for example those relating to illicit dealing (trafficking).

I found that there were many more explanations that related to traffic on communication networks than to vehicles on roads. Many responses were more or less what I expected: the idea of traffic as the quantity of vehicles or pedestrians, or traffic as the quantity of visitors to a website or other service. What was a bit of a surprise at first were the explanations that incorporated the idea of time, as in the following (which are paraphrases of many different responses):

- The aggregation of things (pedestrians or vehicles) coming and going in a particular locality during a specified period of time.
- The number of visitors (for instance, to a web page or website) over a given period.

We can see here the idea of 'traffic' as referring to how busy something is over a particular time period. This makes sense because 'heavy traffic' (for instance) usually implies there are more vehicles or data packets than can be handled comfortably in a particular time period. The same quantity of vehicles or data packets spread over a longer time period might be more manageable. Conversely, increasing the number of vehicles using a network at a particular time can lead to an increase in queues and the delays that occur. The throughput of the network, that is the number of vehicles or packets that are successfully handled per unit time, suffers. In fact, at critical periods only a relatively small increase in the traffic can lead to high levels of congestion.

One approach to network management is to try to spread the demand more evenly, or to redistribute it to less congested parts of the network. With a national road network, the scope that managers have for demand management is currently limited, but more sophisticated techniques are being developed (as we shall see). Nevertheless, traffic information relayed to users of the network can be seen as an indirect way of

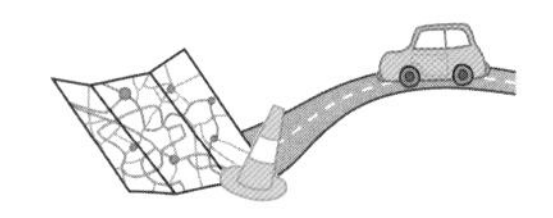

managing demand. In the following subsections we shall look at some ways of informing users of road networks about delays, hazards, diversions, and so on.

2.2 Informing travellers

Information systems have, for some time, been important in journey planning, though their form has changed significantly over recent years. For example, at railway stations and airports, systems that inform passengers of arrivals and departures have always been provided, but now the wider use of ICTs enables individuals to plan their journeys in much greater detail, even before they leave home.

We can think of information supplied to travellers in terms of open-loop control or closed-loop control. The following activity asks you to identify information being used in both these ways.

Activity 5 (self-assessment)

I needed to get to Bristol from the Milton Keynes area, and preferred not to drive. An online rail timetable showed that the only possibilities by train were via Birmingham or London, which would take at least four hours (twice what it would take to drive). I checked another online source to see what coaches were available, and found that I would have to go to Heathrow airport, and change to a coach travelling to Bristol. This was another long journey. I decided to drive, and consulted the journey planner on a motoring organisation's website for a route. I set off by car. On the journey, a traffic report on the car radio warned of a blockage on the motorway I intended to use. I amended my route to avoid using the motorway.

Identify which information was used (by me) in an open-loop way and which in a closed-loop way.

Comment

The answer is given at the end of this part.

Radio Data System (RDS) is a radio system that has been used for some time to deliver information to drivers on the move. RDS can automatically interrupt the broadcast the driver is listening to with local information about traffic problems. In this way, drivers need not miss a traffic announcement if they are tuned to a different station from the one that is carrying the traffic announcement. Some motor car manufacturers have fitted their cars with radios using this system since 1988. The system works because data about a broadcast can be squeezed into a normal radio transmission. At the receiver, this data is separated from the audio part of the transmission. Traffic announcements have a particular

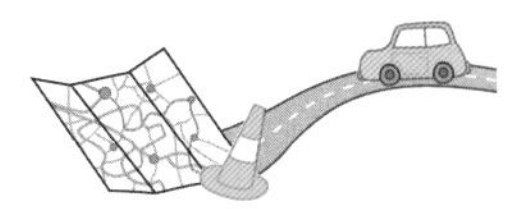

code, which can be registered even if the listener is not listening to the station that carries the announcement (because the receiver can monitor the data incorporated into other stations). If the listener chooses to make use of the traffic announcement facility, which can usually be set 'on' or 'off', these traffic announcements override whatever station the listener is tuned to.

Television is not, of course, appropriate for use whilst travelling (at least by anyone controlling a vehicle). However information relevant to travel plans (such as details of significant sporting events) may be obtained before starting a journey, from services such as Teletext and from a number of interactive digital television services.

Other methods of communicating information to drivers while they are moving are in use or in development at the time of writing. As we will see later, the mobile phone system is used in at least one method of sending traffic data to drivers, and the 3G mobile phone network can also be used to supply internet access to mobile users. At the time of writing, there is much research into the use of microwaves for data communication between vehicles and roadside beacons (and between vehicles and other vehicles).

2.3 Variable message signs

One widely used method of delivering information to motorists while they are travelling is the **variable message sign (VMS)**. Some examples are shown in Figure 4.

variable message sign (VMS)

Besides being a general term for signs like those in Figure 4, Variable Message Signs is the name of a UK company which makes this type of sign. (It made the signs in Figure 4.)

A variable message sign uses large characters (up to 300 to 400 mm high) to warn drivers of approaching problems, for example obstructions, lane closures, bad driving conditions, and so on. Brief indications of likely delay times might be added, and alternative routes suggested. Messages are relayed to the VMS from traffic control centres. They are therefore part of the management system of the road network.

Some signs, referred to as Advanced Motorway Indicators (AMI), are specifically designed to allow a greater degree of control over traffic. They usually include coloured hazard warning symbols and the requirements placed on motorists are often enforced using speed detection and video monitoring equipment. Some AMIs are used to send messages that are specific to individual traffic lanes. An example of this use is where particular lanes need to be closed temporarily.

VMS displays use arrays of light sources so that appropriate groupings of lights can be selected to create the characters or symbols needed in the message. Early designs used individual incandescent lamps, sometimes incorporating mirrors and moving selection mechanisms, but the more recent signs shown in Figure 4 do not rely upon moving parts or incandescent lamps, but instead use light-emitting diodes (LEDs).

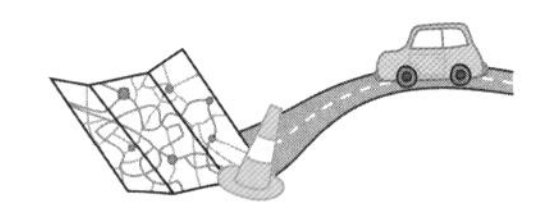

Figure 4 Variable message signs

LEDs are semiconductor devices that you are probably familiar with as indicators on electronic equipment, but they are increasingly used as general light sources. The properties of LEDs also make them attractive for use in traffic light illumination. They are more durable than incandescent lamps and can offer high levels of brightness. Several colours can be used with intensities that can be controlled to suit different lighting and weather conditions. Individual devices can be electronically switched from motorway control centres to create graphical as well as text-based messages.

Activity 6 (exploratory)

What advantages and limitations do roadside and overhead signs have as a way of communicating with the driver as compared with radio announcements?

Comment

One advantage is that roadside and overhead signs can be seen by all users, except where tall lorries occasionally obstruct the line of sight. A limitation is that only fairly short messages can be displayed (it would be dangerous to have long ones). Radio announcements, on the other hand, will be heard only by radio listeners.

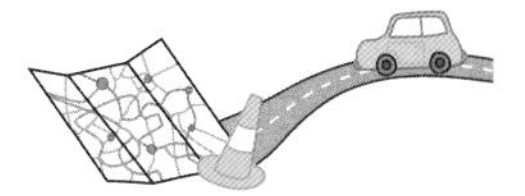

Radio traffic announcements and roadside signs both have the drawback that drivers need to be able to understand the language used. Road traffic is increasingly international. However, other systems can be envisaged in which vehicles have an on-board unit which warns of traffic conditions in response to signals received from roadside transmitters. In principle, these could be multilingual.

2.4 Webcams

I travel regularly between South Wales and Milton Keynes. Before I set off it is often worth my while checking for traffic congestion along the route. I can do this using the internet to access camera images at various locations. These are often referred to as **webcam** images. The term webcam generally refers to inexpensive digital cameras that are often connected directly to personal computers. When supported by suitable software, images from webcams can be loaded into web pages, which can then be accessed by anyone using a web browser. Images can be updated frequently to provide a nearly 'live' view of what is happening in front of the camera.

webcam

Some so-called webcam images actually come from closed-circuit video cameras. Among these are the ones I consult to see the state of the roads along my journey. These images originate from roadside video cameras which transmit moving images of the road to traffic control centres, such as the one in Figure 2. Figure 5 shows the general configuration of such a system.

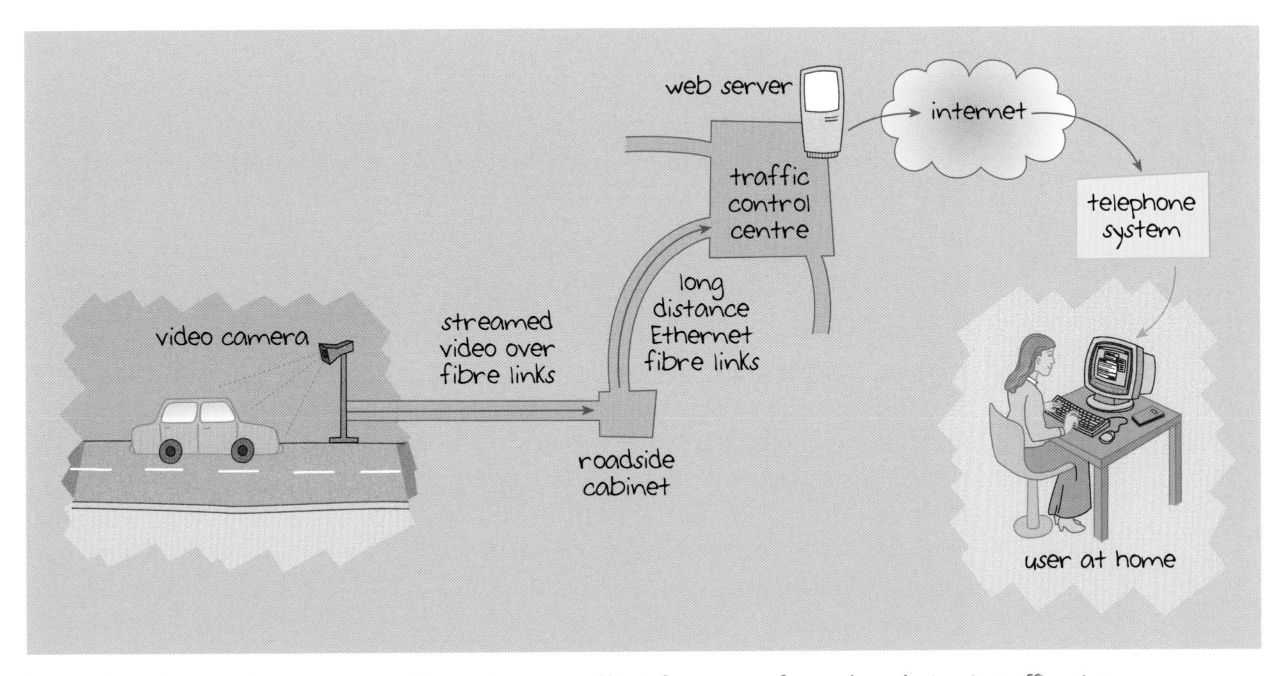

Figure 5 System for creating online webcam traffic information from closed-circuit traffic pictures

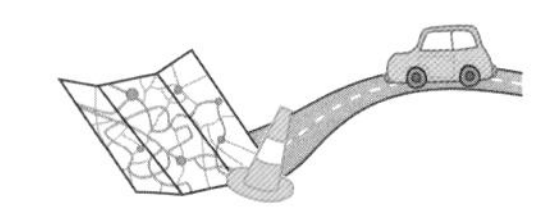

Optical fibres are installed along major roads and motorways. Increasingly, Ethernet is being used to support the transmission of image and other data over the long distances from the roadside to traffic control centres. This allows staff at the control centre to set VMS signs to show appropriate messages about traffic conditions.

Frames from the video-camera images can be sent periodically to a web page on a web server. A motorist using a web browser on a home computer would enter the URL associated with the required video camera location to see the frame currently being displayed.

Some webcam sites are intended for checking weather conditions rather than traffic conditions. Before beginning a journey, it is sometimes worthwhile checking a selection of these as well. The weather could influence the choice of route or departure time, especially during the winter.

You might like to look at some examples of traffic webcam sites. You will find a link to traffic webcams on the T175 website. You may, however, wish to search for webcams that show locations nearer to where you live. If you do this, check how frequently the images are updated. The webcam images that I accessed were updating their images at intervals of about five minutes.

It is possible that developments in on-board computing and networking, to be described later, could enable webcam images to be accessed from within vehicles, though this would not be safe for an unaccompanied driver while moving.

2.5 Summary of Section 2

Many kinds of traffic information can be conveyed by ICTs. I have mentioned just a few here: online timetables, route planners, VMS signs and webcams.

The information might be intended primarily either for users of the network or for managers of the network.

The information might be used in an open-loop way by travellers, for instance for planning a journey before it begins, or in a closed-loop way (to modify the journey while it is happening). For information to be used in a closed-loop way, it needs to be communicated to the traveller during the journey. VMS and RDS are two examples of communication methods that allow information to be passed to drivers during a journey. New methods of communicating with drivers, or with their vehicles, are under development.

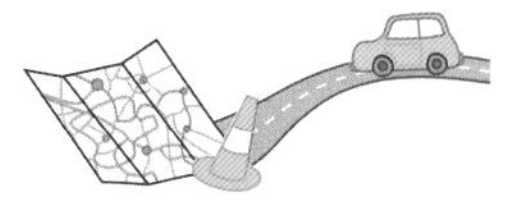

3 Modelling traffic

3.1 Traffic jams from nowhere

It is often helpful to investigate the characteristics and behaviour of a system under varying conditions. Modelling is one means of investigation. Modelling is sometimes carried out by creating physical prototypes, but an alternative approach is to create a mathematical model, or simulation, that can run on computers.

Computer modelling can help us to understand what is happening in different situations. For instance, have you ever been in a road traffic jam for which there is no obvious cause? You might assume that an accident or some other obstacle is the source of the problem, but then, as if by magic, the vehicles in front of you speed up, the problem disappears and no obstacle is apparent.

Activity 7 (self-assessment)

I'm now going to ask you to read a short article that describes the approaches used to create a realistic model of road traffic. The article is entitled 'Bad driving holds the secret to traffic forecasts' (Mullins, 2004). After you have read the article, answer the questions below. Have a look at the questions before you read the article so that you can jot down or highlight the important points as you read through it.

(a) Comment on the article title. In what way does the title relate to the content of the article?

(b) What advantages for this model are cited compared with previous models? (hint: assumptions).

(c) Explain in just a few of your own words the 'pinch effect'.

(d) What problems arise when the information obtained from successful road traffic modelling is made available to many intended users of the road network?

Comment

My answer is given at the end of this part.

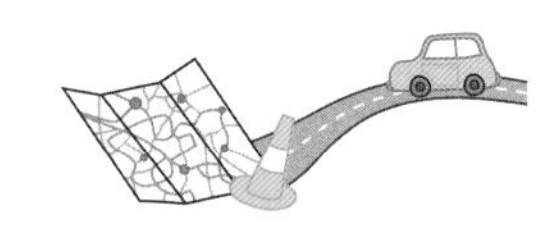

Bad Driving Holds the Secret to Traffic Forecasts

Justin Mullins

July, 2004

New Scientist

When engineers model the way road traffic flows they break the traffic down into three categories: freely flowing, jammed, and an intermediate state called synchronised flow in which dense traffic moves in unison, like marchers moving in step.

But this synchronised flow is unstable. One car pulling into another lane and forcing the driver behind to brake hard is enough to start traffic bunching up. This can quickly develop into a jam that propagates backwards through the traffic like a wave. Failure to predict this 'pinch effect' has stymied past attempts to model traffic flow.

Now Michael Schreckenberg and colleagues at the University of Duisburg-Essen in Germany have developed a computer model that successfully reproduces the pinch effect. 'It is the first model to reproduce all known traffic states,' says team member Robert Barlovic. The team's trick is to be realistic about driver behaviour. 'Real drivers tend to hinder each other when doing things like changing lanes. All this has to be taken into account,' says Schreckenberg. And where previous models have simplified the way cars move – by assuming they can stop immediately without slowing down first, for example – the new model is more sophisticated.

Schreckenberg's computer model divides the road into a regular grid, with one line of cells representing each lane on a highway. Cells in the grid are marked as either containing a vehicle or empty. The number of empty cells between the virtual vehicles depends on the way the drivers are behaving. Accuracy not seen before has been achieved by modelling two behaviours, says Schreckenberg. These are dubbed 'aggressive' behaviour, in which drivers either get too close to the car in front and have to brake, or in which they change lanes too quickly, forcing others to brake. The second behaviour is 'defensive', in which they drive at a generally safe distance.

As the model runs, it moves vehicles according to rules that embody realistic rates of acceleration and deceleration. No infinite decelerations are allowed, for instance. The result is a software model that combines realistic driver behaviour with realistic physics.

The model is already being used to forecast traffic on the autobahn network around the city of Cologne, based on traffic data gathered in real time from sensors buried in the road. Its forecasts, which predict conditions up to an hour ahead, are displayed on the web at www.autobahn.nrw.de. More than 90 per cent of [the] time, it correctly predicts traffic density.

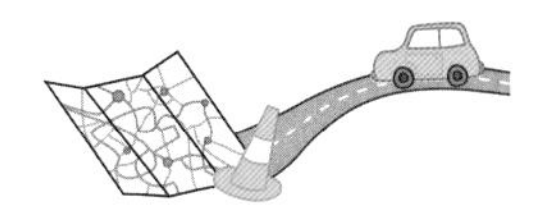

> But the website has already become a victim of its own success, admits Schreckenberg. Some of the 300,000 people a day who are visiting the site are replanning their journeys on the basis of its forecasts, and this is beginning to make the forecasts themselves less accurate. And soon it could get even worse when the website becomes available on 3G cellphones, he says.
>
> So the researchers are now trying to adjust the way the traffic information is provided to drivers to take this destructive effect into account. One idea, says Schreckenberg, might actually be to provide less complete traffic information to encourage drivers to adopt more varied strategies for evading congestion, so they do not all flock to the same exits.

The article that you have just studied serves to emphasise how modelling of the variability of human behaviour can be difficult and could be self-defeating if it produces behaviour which itself causes new problems to arise. Human beings do not necessarily behave in a way that is orderly or for the greater good. The term 'messy behaviour' is sometimes used in this context.

An interesting example of a strategy to control the variability of driving behaviour is the application of variable speed limits imposed on the M25 circular motorway around London in the UK. The speed restrictions in force are indicated on variable message signs situated at regular intervals along the motorway. The speed limits are enforced strictly using speed cameras. The idea is to reduce the erratic start/stop cycles of vehicles and the build-up of 'pinch-effect' congestion. A further benefit claimed is that of reducing the emissions associated with erratic traffic flow.

Of course, traffic jams can also arise as a result of static obstructions. A clear example would be when an accident causes complete or partial blocking of a road. The normal throughput of traffic would be affected, leading to larger than normal queues and longer than normal delays.

There are many features of a road network where some sort of queuing is normal and to be expected. Examples of what I am thinking about here include any type of road junction, including where traffic lights and roundabouts are positioned, motorway or bridge tolling points, and so on. In fact queues and queuing systems are to be found in many day-to-day situations, though you may not have thought about them as queuing systems.

3.2 Queuing

In general, queues form when 'things' have to wait for what we can generally refer to as a 'service'. I say 'things' because this could include people waiting for a bus, vehicles at traffic lights, or items being manufactured on a production line that need some further process to be carried out on them. A service in this context could be, for instance, getting served in a post office queue; but it could also be simply passing what I shall call a service point, such as a roundabout or a road junction.

Service points are more generally referred to as servers in queue modelling. (The term server is also used to describe computers that provide a particular service, such as a web server or print server.)

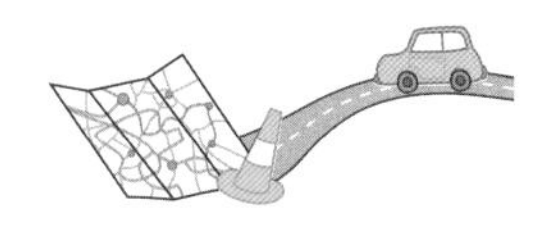

Activity 8 (exploratory)

Think of an example of a queue that you observed or were part of during the last week or so. Identify the service being provided and how many service points there were in your example. Briefly describe the arrangement and comment upon how well it worked.

Comment

I thought of an instance where I travelled by rail and needed to buy a ticket just before departure. A fairly long queue fed four serving hatches (service points). Whenever a serving hatch became free the person at the front of the queue moved forward to be served. I was keen to get my ticket quickly so that I would not miss my train. The arrangement seemed to be fairer than say supermarket queues, where it's up to the customer to select which queue to join, each queue generally leading to one service point only. This could involve a higher risk of delay if I was unlucky enough to have chosen the wrong queue.

Queuing is common in all transport systems, not just road transport. For instance, busy airports often use queuing systems to manage the arrival of aeroplanes. When runways used for arrivals are busy, aeroplanes waiting to land are stacked or layered in circulating paths at different altitudes close to the airport, until they can be called down. Queuing will also occur on the ground for aeroplanes waiting to depart from a busy airport. Other examples include trains waiting for a free platform.

buffer

buffer store

The basic elements of a queuing system are depicted in Figure 6. There is a service point and a stream of arrivals. Between them is a **buffer**, or **buffer store**. This is a short-term storage area which holds a queue of arrivals waiting to be served. (In a communication network, the buffer will be some locations in an electronic memory or store.)

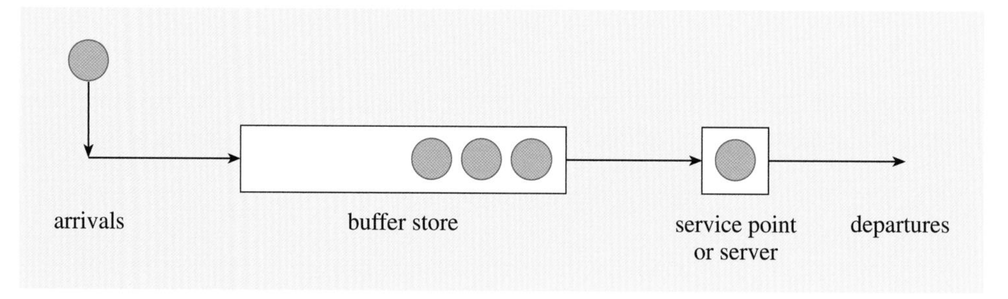

Figure 6 Queuing system

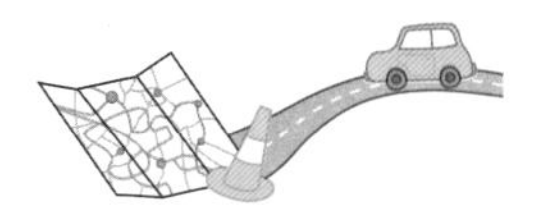

Activity 9 (self-assessment)

A service can handle up to 30 vehicles per hour arriving at regular intervals. Depending on the time of day, vehicles arrive regularly at the following rates:

- 20 vehicles per hour.
- 30 vehicles per hour.
- 40 vehicles per hour.

(a) Which of the three rates will cause a queue to develop?

(b) If the system starts with a queue, explain briefly whether the queue will grow, shrink or remain the same for each of the three arrival rates given above.

Comment

The answer is given at the end of this part.

In queuing systems a full buffer means that there is no storage available. In the case of a queuing system handling data packets, if the buffer was full then the packets would be lost because there is nowhere for them to be stored. When we think of other things being queued, such as vehicles, then if there is no waiting area left, vehicles must be sent somewhere else. They can't simply vanish. The box 'Buffer overflow' is an anecdote about a full buffer in a context where arriving traffic could not be redirected.

Buffer overflow

I remember many years ago being on a long escalator in Charles de Gaulle airport in France, where neither I, nor the people around me, could see the arrival point from the starting point of the escalator. A rather frightening experience followed when I, along with many other travellers, progressed towards the end and realised that this area was obstructed by a large crowd of people who were unable to move forward. The 'buffer' was full and there did not seem to be any off switch to halt the relentless flow of people!

In such physical queuing systems the arrival of human beings at a point, where there is insufficient storage or waiting space available, is a problem. Human beings can't simply vanish in the same way data packets can! Clearly I survived the uncomfortable ordeal, but I've since been a lot more cautious when encountering busy escalators.

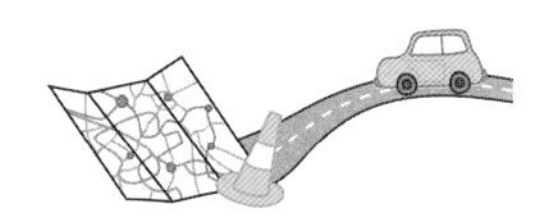

3.3 Queuing in data communication networks

As mentioned above, queues are likely to develop when the service can't keep pace with the demand for it. One technological area where queues were first investigated was telecommunications (conventional telephone services), where, at certain times of the day, the capacity of a network might be unable to provide connections to all those people attempting to make telephone calls. This led to the development of queuing theory.

In modern digital communications, it is sometimes necessary to model how packets of data are queued. For instance, at routers and bridges the destination address of a packet is used to determine the next link on the route that the packet will take. This process takes time. Packets can arrive at a network node at a certain rate, be stored and then sent onto another link ('served') at another rate. To model this realistically the different patterns of arrival and service times associated with such 'store and forward' packet switching would need to be carefully evaluated.

Buffer sizes need to be chosen so that the queuing system can accept and store the packets until they can be dealt with by the service point (whatever form this takes). When traffic is likely to be variable, a buffer needs to accommodate the periods of heavy traffic. For a given situation, increasing the buffer size means that there is more room to accommodate a larger number of packets. However, if packets are stored and then processed by the service point in the order in which they are received, then the more packets that are stored, the longer the delay is likely to be between joining the end of the queue and being served.

You should now be able to appreciate how important queuing systems are in data communication networks, where data packets are often of different lengths and sent in irregular bursts.

Activity 10 (exploratory)

I have referred to the importance of choosing a sufficiently large buffer size to accommodate variations in traffic. What other feature of a queuing system could be changed to help reduce the delays and also the possibility that packets would be lost? Hint: it may help to think of what happens in some busy shops and ticket offices.

Comment

The number of service points (or servers) could be increased. In a busy shop people waiting in a long queue to pay for their purchases would probably be delighted to see another till opened. However,

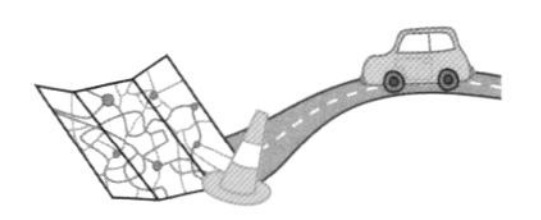

having lots of service points (or tills open) would be inefficient during quieter periods, whether data packets or people were in the queue.

Another possibility is to increase the speed of service of individual servers.

3.4 Simulating queues

I'm now going to return to queuing in road networks. The purpose of the next activity is to show how queues can form even when, in a perfect world, the service arrangements might seem to have been adequately provided for.

The activity is based on the *Queue simulation* software, which you will find on the course DVD. It simulates the entrance to a petrol station, which has only one pump. Vehicles on a main road where stopping is forbidden (a 'clearway' in the UK) are attempting to join a slip road leading to the forecourt of the petrol station. The slip road is in effect the buffer, where vehicles can wait to use the petrol pump.

For convenience we shall assume that all vehicles on the main road travelling in the direction shown need refuelling, but can stop only if there is room on the slip road (or at the petrol pump).

The length of any queue that forms on the slip road is determined by the arrival rate of vehicles joining the slip road, as well as the rate at which vehicles are served. By 'rate' I mean the number per unit of time; in this simulation that means the number per hour.

I am taking the term 'served' to include the complete set of activities that could occur when a customer's vehicle is at the pump position. This would include dispensing and paying for the fuel (and any other goods) and preparing to leave the pump position.

When the slip road is full of queuing vehicles, vehicles on the main road that would otherwise have stopped cannot do so. They simply continue on their journey. They have been lost to this queuing system.

The simulator has a window in which both the arrival rate and service rate can be varied. The service rate has an initial setting of 5 vehicles per hour. However, one hour is simulated in 10 seconds so that you don't need to spend a lot of time waiting. Both the arrival rate and the service rate can be set to 'regular' or 'random' mode. Regular, for arrivals, refers to equal time intervals between vehicles arriving, whereas random refers to irregular and unpredictable time intervals between arrivals. For service, regular relates to equal time intervals at the pump for each driver being served, while random relates to irregular and unpredictable time intervals for each driver being served.

Another parameter that you will need to take note of on the simulator window is the 'lost' counter.

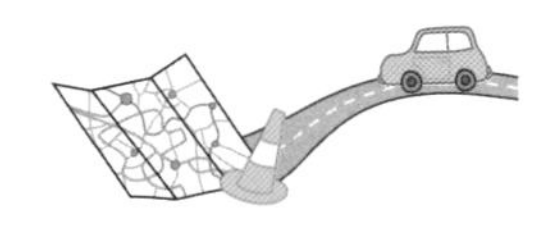

Activity 11 (exploratory)

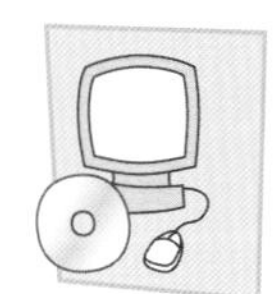

To carry out this activity you will need to run the *Queue simulation* software from the T175 DVD. Start the simulator now so that you can see the main simulator window.

(a) Familiarise yourself with the features of the simulation.

(b) Set up the starting conditions shown in Row 1 of Table 3. That is, set the arrival mode to 'regular' and the arrival rate to '4 per hour'. Set the service mode to 'regular' and the service rate to '5 per hour'. Check that the run time (in the 'Run settings' menu) is set to 2 hours. Now press 'Run' for the simulator to operate. After the simulator has finished running enter the results for 'served', 'lost' and 'queued' in Row 1 of Table 3.

(c) Repeat process (b) for each of Rows 2–5, using the arrival rates shown in Rows 2–5. Enter the results in Rows 2–5 as appropriate. You should find that as the arrival rate increases, there comes a point where a vehicle is lost. Note the value of arrival rate when just one car is lost. You will need to use this value of arrival in the remaining parts of this activity.

(d) Set the simulator to the settings in Row 6. For the arrival rate x, use the value you identified in (c), at which just one car was lost. Record your results in Row 6.

(e) Because the arrival rate in (d) was random, repeated runs with those settings will almost certainly give different results. With the settings used in (d), run the simulator four more times and record your results in Rows 7–10.

(f) Set the simulator to the settings in Row 11. (Use the same value for x, the arrival rate, that you used in Rows 6–10.) Record your results in Row 11; then run the simulator four more times with the same settings, putting your results in Rows 12–15.

(g) Set the simulator to the values in Row 16. (Use the same value for x, the arrival rate, that you used in rows 6 to 10.) Record your results in row 16; then run the simulator four more times with the same settings, putting your results in Rows 17–20.

(h) When you have completed your table comment on:

  (i) The variations in lost vehicles that occurred in each of the four series of runs.

  (ii) What you think the implications are in terms of buffer size and the delays for motorists waiting to fill up.

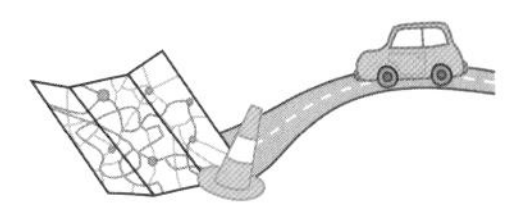

Table 3

	Arrival		Service		Results		
Row	**Mode**	**Rate (per hour)**	**Mode**	**Rate (per hour)**	**Served**	**Lost**	**Queued**
1	Regular	4	Regular	5			
2	Regular	5	Regular	5			
3	Regular	6	Regular	5			
4	Regular	7	Regular	5			
5	Regular	8	Regular	5			
6	Random	x	Regular	5			
7	Random	x	Regular	5			
8	Random	x	Regular	5			
9	Random	x	Regular	5			
10	Random	x	Regular	5			
11	Regular	x	Random	5			
12	Regular	x	Random	5			
13	Regular	x	Random	5			
14	Regular	x	Random	5			
15	Regular	x	Random	5			
16	Random	x	Random	5			
17	Random	x	Random	5			
18	Random	x	Random	5			
19	Random	x	Random	5			
20	Random	x	Random	5			

Comment

I can't comment on your results, but my own experiences were as follows.

(i) With regular arrival and regular service (Rows 1–5), the queuing system operated without loss of vehicles until the arrival rate exceeded the service rate and the buffer filled during the run time. I found that when an arrival rate of 7 vehicles per hour was reached the buffer size of 4 (the maximum number of vehicles waiting to approach the fuel pump) was insufficient and one vehicle was lost. I used an arrival rate of 7 vehicles per hour for x in rows 6–20.

When the arrival rate was random but the service rate was regular (Rows 6–10) a vehicle was sometimes, but not always, lost.

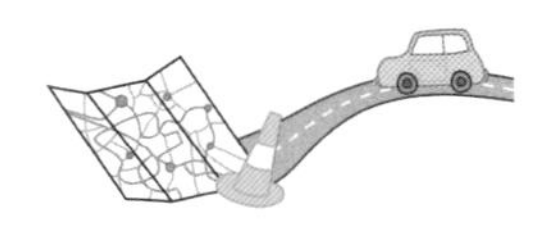

When the arrival rate was regular but the service rate was random (Rows 11–15) vehicles were almost always lost. In my tests I recorded up to 5 vehicles lost in one run. You should have been able to detect similar trends in your results as they depend upon the characteristics of the simulation model (specifically, on the statistical variations that are allowed to occur in the 'random' settings).

When the arrival rate and the service rate were both random (Rows 16–20) I found a wide variation in the numbers of vehicles lost (from 0 to 5).

(ii) To minimise vehicle loss, the buffer size needs to be increased, especially when both arrivals and service are random. From this simple simulation we cannot say by how much the buffer should be increased. In my results I reported losing up to five vehicles, but this does not mean that increasing the buffer size from 4 vehicles to 9 vehicles would guarantee no loss of vehicles. In fact, however big the buffer is, there is always a possibility of vehicles being lost, although the larger the buffer the rarer the losses become. (However, a large buffer increases the waiting periods as longer queues form.) To decide on a suitable buffer size we would need a realistic prediction of the patterns (or distributions) of arrivals and service, and a decision on how many losses we could tolerate.

Although a queuing system should work well when arrivals and service follow regular patterns, this is unrealistic because in real life vehicles (or people) joining queues will not appear so uniformly. Nor will they be served at uniform rates. Therefore queuing systems must be able to cater for these uncertainties and the design of a buffer must take into account the variations that are likely to occur.

Activity 12 (self-assessment)

Packets are known to arrive at an average rate of 10 000 per hour at a particular node in a communication network. Designers assume that the packets arrive regularly and choose a buffer size accordingly. When the performance of the system is tested, however, packets are frequently lost. What could be the cause of the problem here?

Comment

The answer is given at the end of this part.

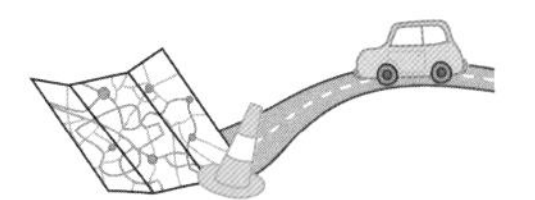

3.5 Summary of Section 3

I would like to pause at this point to summarise the main ideas in Section 3 before we move on.

Congestion occurs in communication and transport networks when too many users are attempting to use a limited resource. Queuing can arise because of restrictions (or obstacles) that occur at features of a network – whether nodes in a communication network or roundabouts in a road network. The irregularity of arrival and service processes is significant in determining how congested a part of the network may become.

In road networks we have also seen an example of how irregularity (or randomness) in the behaviour of human drivers can seed congestion when there is no obvious physical obstruction. Under these conditions the vehicle and the human driver can be seen as part of a road transport system needing to be controlled and this includes the problem of controlling individual driving behaviour.

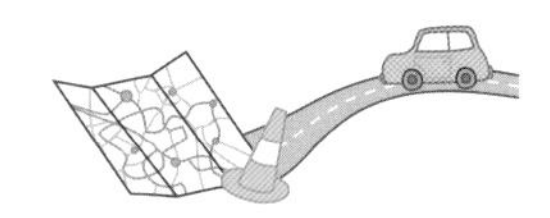

4 Charging methods

4.1 Charging for resources

A common way of managing a resource is by charging for its use. Charging based on the degree of use of a resource is fairly common. My electricity bill, for example, is strongly based upon the number of electrical units that I use in a billing period. The more electricity I use, the larger is my bill. Some resources are charged at a flat rate. For instance, the cost of posting a letter within a country is usually fixed, irrespective of how far the letter has to travel (although there are different prices for different weight or size ranges). A mixture of charging methods is also common. Thus, although my electricity bill depends on the amount of electricity I use, it also includes a fixed charge which I have to pay irrespective of whether I use any electricity at all.

The next activity asks you to comment on the charging methods used in each case.

Activity 13 (exploratory)

On what basis are you charged when you make use of the following services provided by various networks?

(a) Gas and water supplied to your home.

(b) Making a telephone call on the public switched telephone network.

(c) Making a journey on a railway network.

(d) Using your own car on a road network.

Comment

(a) Domestic use of gas is usually charged in a similar way to electricity, with the greater part of it being by consumption, but with a standing charge element. Water, in some countries or in some areas, may still be charged at a flat rate, meaning that charges do not depend upon the usage (within reasonable limits). Increasingly though, water is metered and charged according to the volume that is used.

(b) Telephone calls may be charged based on the duration of the call. Alternatively many other tariff combinations are offered based upon a quarterly charge that is largely independent of the duration of the calls.

(c) For railway travel a ticket generally needs to be bought for each journey and is often, though not always, based upon the journey length and time of travel, possibly the class of service and in some countries, the train type.

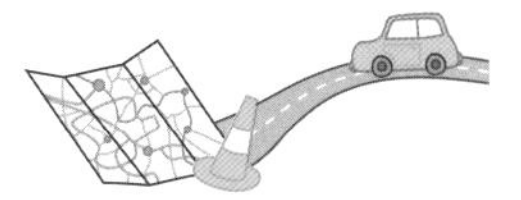

(d) With a car, there is a high initial cost involved in buying it and an annual fixed charge to tax it. The expenditure on petrol relates to the distance driven – the further you drive, the more you pay for a given engine capacity.

Traditionally, in the UK, there has been no charge based directly on use of the road network itself, except for occasional toll roads and toll bridges. The idea of charging for road use has gained ground, though, because it potentially offers a way of controlling congestion and because ICTs make automatic road-charging schemes feasible on a large scale. The latter point is particularly important; ideally, road charging should cause minimal or no disruption to the use of the network.

Various types of road-charging scheme have been proposed or are in use. They can be divided into three main types:

- Charging for driving within a particular zone. The charge is independent of the amount of driving done within the zone. A number of schemes like this operate, in various parts of the world, although they are not yet common in the UK.
- Charging for driving along a stretch of road, or for using a bridge or tunnel. This is the traditional toll system occasionally found in the UK but quite common on Continental European motorways.
- Charging according to the distance driven anywhere within a large area such as a country.

At the time of writing, the last of the three types above is quite rare. In some parts of Switzerland and Austria, lorries pay a charge according to the distance they have driven. (Distance data is obtained from the tachograph, which lorries are obliged to carry.) However, the long-term ambition of many governments is to introduce road charging by distance or, more precisely, variable road charging by distance. We shall look at this option in more depth in Section 5.

A tachograph records a vehicle's speed and the times at which it was driven.

Activity 14 (exploratory)

In a particular city, drivers are charged a flat fee every time they enter a city-centre zone. Bills are sent to drivers four times a year. Bills itemise the drivers' use of the zone. Suggest the types of information the operators of the system need in order to create itemised bills.

Comment

The main requirements would include information about the identity of the vehicle (including the type of vehicle if there are different charging rates for, say, cars, vans and lorries); details about the owner (or keeper) including billing-related information such as name, address, possibly bank account and so on; dates and times when the zone was used.

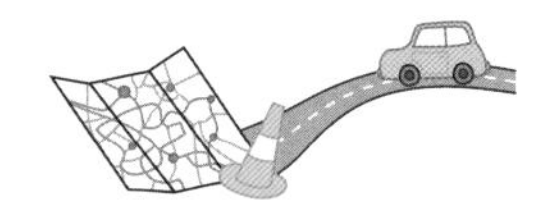

In the UK, a pioneering road-charging scheme is the Central London Congestion Charging scheme (see box). A small-scale system operates in central Durham.

The Central London Congestion Charging scheme

The Central London Congestion Charging scheme, introduced in 2003, has no toll booths or barriers, but uses automatic number plate recognition (ANPR) to identify vehicles entering the controlled area. The vehicles themselves do not carry any extra equipment related to the charging scheme. Multiple cameras (to capture number plate images) are placed at all access points to the charging area. The London scheme started with banks of cameras at 174 of the charging zone's entry and exit points.

As introduced, the scheme uses transmitted analogue video information over optical fibres from the cameras to a centralised processing location. The received images are therefore in effect, real-time video links rather than being based upon digital techniques. When the scheme was first planned there were no similar schemes in existence and so the approach was to use mature technologies that had been well tried and tested. Now that the scheme has become established, new developments are likely. Digitisation of the images at the monitoring points is one possibility.

Initially, successful number plate identification averaged between 70% and 80%, but in 2005 reported success rates were around 90%. The success rate of number plate recognition will undoubtedly improve due to developments in software and other factors, such as the stricter control of number plate fonts.

The London congestion charging scheme requires the purchase of permits prior to, or on the day of, use. Drivers who do not purchase a permit but are identified by the system are penalised by being sent a bill which (at the time of writing) is more than ten times the cost of a one-day permit.

Other ways of identifying vehicles for road-charging schemes can involve the use of electronic tagging devices attached to windscreens. As a vehicle enters a city centre, for example, the electronic tag is detected by roadside equipment. The tag sends identification details to the roadside receiver, and from there data passes to a central processing office. The driver's account is debited by the appropriate amount. (This type of system is currently used in several towns in Norway.) Similar systems are available for frequent users of toll roads, tunnels and bridges. At the entrance to the tolled section, a detector on an overhead gantry collects identification data from tags attached to vehicles enrolled in the scheme. These vehicles can pass straight through the toll booths without having to stop, unlike other vehicles whose drivers have to stop and hand over cash.

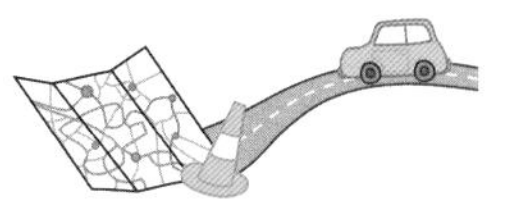

4.2 Automatic number plate recognition (ANPR)

We saw in the last section the need to be able to identify vehicles for some types of automated road charging. Number plate recognition offers several benefits as a way if identifying vehicles. In the UK the Driver and Vehicle Licensing Agency (DVLA) database holds information linking the vehicle registration (the number on the number plate) to the chassis identity, the type of vehicle, other technical specifications, and the keeper's name and address (the keeper is usually the owner too). By linking the number plate recognition system to the DVLA database, a lot of the basic information needed for billing the road user can be obtained automatically. This means that, unlike the various tagging systems mentioned at the end of the last section, the vehicle does not need to be registered with the charging system, and does not need to carry special devices, such as an electronic tag.

I don't intend to go into specific technical details about how number plates are read. Instead, I want to think in a broad way about how an ANPR system might operate by considering a hypothetical system. The system I shall explore is not the same as the system used in the Central London Congestion Charging scheme, although it has some points of similarity. I am going to explore this imaginary scheme because we can often gain a useful insight into a problem by thinking about how it would break down into smaller tasks. I shall show you what I mean, by posing the questions that a detection and recognition system would need to resolve. The general configuration of my hypothetical ANPR system is shown in Figure 7.

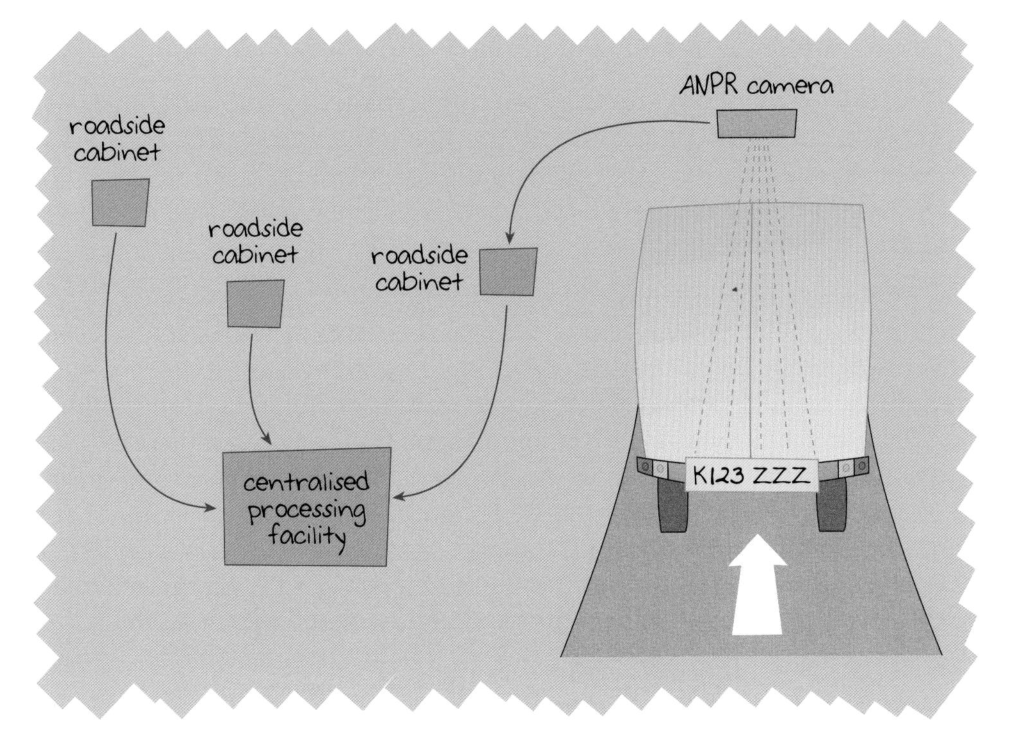

Figure 7 ANPR system

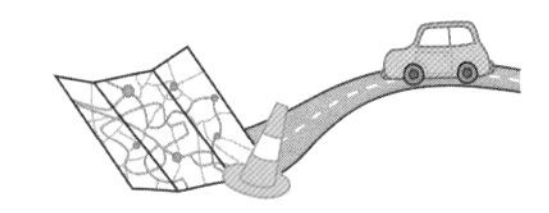

An ANPR system captures images of passing vehicles. Data is sent to a roadside cabinet. From there the data goes to a central processing facility, which receives data from all the cameras in the scheme. At the central processing facility, registration numbers are checked against a database of vehicles so that bills can be created.

The first part of the process of capturing number plate data is detecting the presence of a vehicle passing the camera. There are several ways of doing this.

If a vehicle is known to be present and an image of the front or rear of the vehicle is captured, then the next task could be to locate the number plate within the image area.

The final stage is concerned with reading the registration number from the number plate. Once the location of the number plate itself had been determined, the characters that make up the vehicle registration would need to be identified reliably.

I will discuss these stages in the following subsections, starting with detecting the presence of the vehicle.

4.3 Detecting vehicles

Table 4 shows some of the technologies that can be used for the detection of vehicles passing a monitoring point. All these are non-contact technologies – that is, they do not rely upon making any direct physical contact with vehicles. They are also all passive; that is, they do not require the vehicle to have an on-board transmitter, to which a roadside detector might respond.

The rows in Table 4 are arranged to bring together technologies that have some common characteristics. The first three rows (radar and microwave, optical, and infrared technologies) make use of different regions of the electromagnetic spectrum. All three can be used to detect vehicles and their speeds.

The next two rows (inductive loop and magnetic) can be grouped because they both detect changes occurring at relatively low frequency as vehicles move across the detection zone. Inductive loops are commonly used to detect vehicles approaching traffic lights and work on the basis that an electrical voltage is generated when a mostly ferrous body (that is, containing iron or steel) passes close to a conducting loop of wire. Magnetic detection relies on local changes in the Earth's magnetic field patterns caused by the presence of a vehicle. You may have noticed that reading a compass inside a car can be very unreliable because of the way in which a car distorts the natural magnetic field.

The last two rows (acoustic and ultrasonic) both rely on sound waves. Sound waves are pressure waves that rely on the 'springiness' of the air between the detector and the vehicle. These are fundamentally different

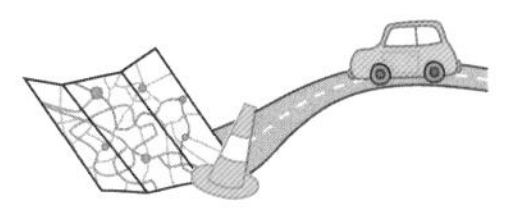

waves from electromagnetic waves, which can travel through space in the absence of any air.

Table 4 Technologies used to detect vehicles

Technology	Description
Radar and microwave	High-frequency (microwave) electromagnetic radiation directed at the vehicle is reflected from the vehicle (a similar process to the radar detection of aeroplanes by reflected radiation). The part of the electromagnetic spectrum used can provide detection under poor weather conditions (just as an aeroplane can be safely landed without direct visibility of the runway). The radiation is concentrated into narrow beams that can be used to measure a vehicle's speed directly.
Optical / video imaging	Visible light is used to capture and then process images. Not suited to all weather or lighting conditions. The frequency of light is much higher than the microwave frequencies used for radar.
Infrared	Infrared can be used in a similar way to optical sensing, but provides superior performance in some weather conditions such as fog. In addition a vehicle can be illuminated with infrared 'light' without the driver being aware of it or distracted by it, because it is invisible to humans. Hence vehicle registrations can be read in darkness. Infrared frequencies are just below those of the visible spectrum.
Inductive loop	An insulated, electrically conducting loop is installed under the road surface. An electrical signal is generated in the loop when a vehicle passes. Can be used to count vehicles passing or arriving at a point. Can be damaged by heavy vehicles.
Magnetic	The local strength and direction of the Earth's magnetic field is changed by the presence of a vehicle with an appreciable iron or steel content. Detection of small vehicles and bicycles is possible, though separating vehicles that are travelling close together may be difficult.
Acoustic	This technique can distinguish between the sounds made by different vehicles (acoustic signatures) as they pass (just as humans can). Relies upon signal processing to filter out irrelevant background noises and identify particular types of vehicle.
Ultrasonic	'Sound' energy at much higher frequencies than humans can hear is transmitted to and reflected from the vehicle to be detected. However this technique is sensitive to temperature and air turbulence of the sort that quickly travelling vehicles create.

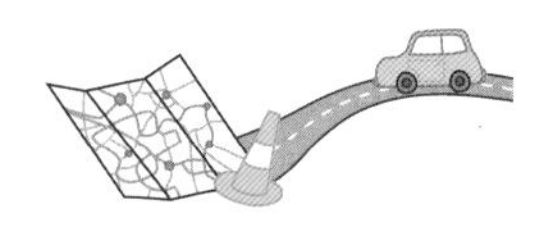

Activity 15 (self-assessment)

All the technologies in Table 4 can be used to detect vehicles, but not all of them can be used for both detecting and identifying a vehicle. Which ones can be used for both these functions? (By 'identify' I mean uniquely identify, rather than, say, identifying a particular make of vehicle.)

Comment

The answer is given at the end of this part.

For identifying vehicles by their number plates, the optical/video imaging and the infrared technologies are the ones to choose. The ability of infrared to operate in adverse weather gives it an advantage over the optical/video techniques.

You may have noticed many devices that look like conventional cameras mounted on motorway gantries or on tall, blue poles on major roads in the UK. These are likely to be infrared detectors of the sort I have been describing. Figure 8 is an example of one.

Figure 8 Roadside camera used for monitoring traffic flow

Note that all these methods of detection and identification are, as I mentioned earlier, passive. There are also active methods, some of which have already been mentioned. For instance, all vehicles could carry a small transmitter that sends out a signal with a coded representation of its registration number. Active methods depend on signals being sent out from the vehicle to a receiver, rather than on energy being reflected back to a detector or the car having a magnetic or electrical effect.

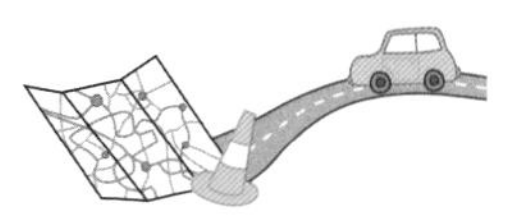

4.4 Reading number plates

Once a vehicle has been detected, a sequence of images can be taken of the front or rear of the vehicle. A suitable single frame can be selected from a sequence of images for analysis in order to find the registration number.

In a film camera, an image is focused onto an optically sensitive surface – a celluloid film. In a digital camera the sensitive surface is an array of sensors which are sensitive to visible light. In an infrared digital camera the array of sensors is sensitive to infrared radiation. The image detail will depend on how the radiation is focused onto the sensor array, and the number of sensitive elements that make up the array. We can think of each sensitive element as providing one pixel of the image. One format used for this purpose has 768 × 288 pixels to represent a complete image frame (the longer side is horizontal).

An image produced by an infrared detector does not have the colour variation of visible light, so the image is monochrome. Each pixel can be represented by a number representing its shade of grey. A typical scale would identify 256 different levels of greyness.

It would be very convenient if each vehicle's number plate was at some fixed position relative to the camera, but in practice, even if all number plates were at a prescribed height, a vehicle's position on the road could vary considerably. Thus the software responsible for identifying the number plate needs to be able to make judgements about where the number plate is. Software capable of shape and pattern recognition has been developed for other applications such as the identification of components to be assembled by robots in manufacturing plants. However, to be sure of including the complete number plate, captured images would need to be much larger than the number plate area alone. The pattern-recognition software would then need to scan the image in order to identify the area showing the vehicle's number plate.

Having located the number plate, the next task is to read it. Character recognition software has been available for some time now. One application can be run on a **tablet PC** (Figure 9), such as the one I am writing this on. In fact it can recognise my handwriting reasonably accurately and change it into standard text characters (Figure 10).

tablet PC

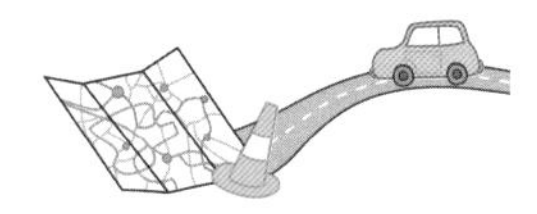

Figure 9 Tablet PC

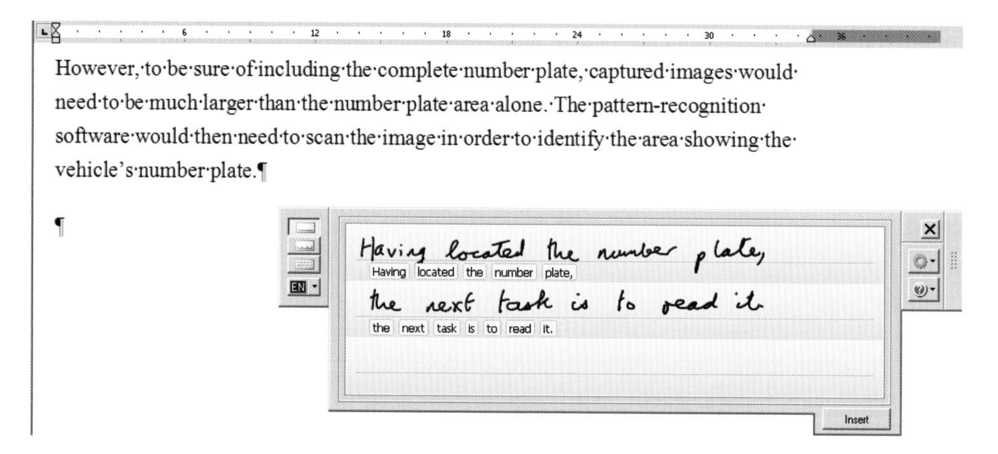

Figure 10 Character recognition by a tablet PC. Handwriting in the inner window is automatically converted to text during writing. The converted text can be edited, corrected, and inserted into a word processor document

4.5 Processing and sending data

Once an image of a passing car has been captured, it needs to be processed so that the registration number can be read from it automatically. This processing could be done locally (at the roadside cabinet near the camera) or at the central processing facility. Either option has advantages and disadvantages, and we shall explore some of them in this section.

One option is to send streams of data representing complete captured images like that of Figure 11 to the centralised processing facility. This is similar to what happens in the London congestion-charging system, where video signals are sent for processing centrally. If data is to be processed centrally, a digital communication link would need to be able to carry a large amount of data for each complete image.

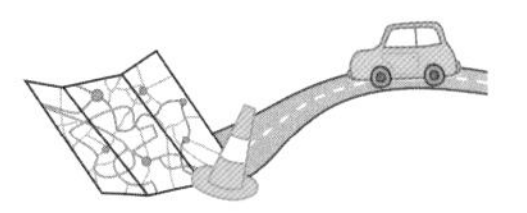

Figure 11 Number plate image

Another option is to carry out some or all of the processing in the roadside cabinets near the cameras. This reduces the amount of data to be transmitted to a central processing facility, but the roadside installations will be more complex and more expensive.

I will start with the first option outlined above, in which all the processing is done centrally and none is done at the roadside. I shall suppose that vehicles pass an ANPR camera at a rate of up to two vehicles per second in each of three separate lanes. An image similar to that of Figure 11 is captured for each vehicle and then coded using a 256-level greyscale. A format of 768×288 pixels is used to represent each image frame.

In the next few activities you will carry out some calculations for this scenario.

Activity 16 (self-assessment)

Calculate the total number of bits required to represent one complete image frame, assuming that no compression is used.

Comment

The answer is given at the end of this part.

Activity 17 (self-assessment)

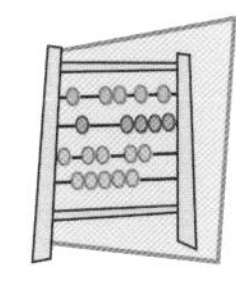

For the system in Activity 16, what would be the minimum data rate needed (expressed in bits per second) to transmit all the image data (from all three lanes) to the centralised computer without using compression?

Comment

The answer is given at the end of this part.

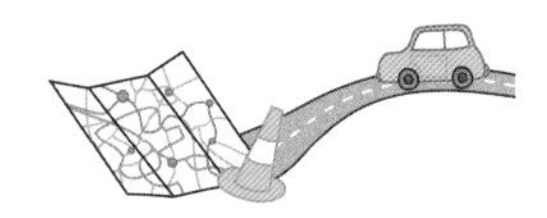

The answer to Activity 17 is a fairly high data rate – several times larger than domestic broadband, for instance. A scheme based on this method would probably require dedicated data links.

The next step is to see how much this data rate can be reduced by doing some of the processing in roadside installations near the cameras.

One possibility is for the roadside installation to work out which part of the picture is the number plate, and to send only that part for central processing. Because the number plate is a small part of the picture, the amount of data that would have to be sent for each car is less than if the whole picture were sent.

Activity 18 asks you to work out the ratio of the area of the whole picture to the area of the part which shows the number plate. This is the first step to finding the new data rate. If you are not familiar with ratios, you might find the box 'Ratios' useful.

Ratios

A ratio expresses a proportional relationship between two or more things. An example is 15:1 (fifteen to one) and this could relate, for example, to the ratio of students to tutors for an Open University course. A particular region may have 30 students studying the course, with two tutors to guide them, but the ratio of students to tutors would still be 15:1. In other words, the ratio is not affected if both sides are multiplied or divided by the same amount. The following ratios are all the same:

60:4 30:2 15:1 7.5:0.5

This example shows that ratios do not have to use whole numbers.

In using ratios care is needed to put the things being represented in the right order. It would, for instance, be incorrect to say that the ratio of the number of tutors to students was 15:1, because this would mean that there were 15 tutors to each student on a course. The ratio of tutors to students should be stated as 1:15.

Ratios are usually notated with a colon in the middle, but an oblique line can be used. For example, a ratio 1:20 can be written 1/20. This highlights the relationship between ratios and fractions. If a quantity is in a ratio of 1:20 to something else, then the first quantity is one-twentieth of the second.

The ratios in this box are mostly whole numbers, which are convenient and easy to relate to. However ratios and proportions can also be expressed using fractions or decimals. For example, an alternative way to express a ratio of 1:20 would be 0.05:1. Here I have divided each number in the ratio by 20, and 1/20 is 0.05.

Activity 18 (self-assessment)

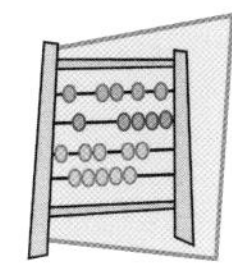

From Figure 11, work out the ratio of the area of the whole picture to the area of the number plate. (Hint: Use a ruler to make approximate measurements of the whole image and then of the part of the image corresponding to the number plate. Assume the number plate can be treated as a rectangle. Calculate the two areas and compare them.)

Comment

The answer is given at the end of this part.

The next task is to find what the new data rate will be if we transmit images of just the number plate, rather than the whole picture. Fortunately this particular example is fairly simple to deal with. In the simplest analysis (and without compression) the data required to represent an image is proportional to the area of the image. If we send just an image of the number plate, we need send only a twenty-third of the data we sent before, because the number plate area is a twenty-third of the whole picture area. And this applies to all six of the number plates we send per second. The data rate is therefore, one twenty-third of 11 Mbps, which is, to two significant figures, 0.48 Mbps.

This example turned out to be simple because the ratio of 23:1 enables us to see immediately that the new data rate is one twenty-third of the old one.

Sometimes calculations involving ratios are a little more complicated than the one above, for example if the ratio appears in an equation. The box 'Ratios in equations' shows you a way of dealing with this sort of case.

Ratios in equations

Ratios can be used in equations, and this allows unknown values to be calculated from what is already known. For instance, if r is the unknown term in a ratio of $11{:}r$, which we happen to know has a value of 23:1, then

$$11{:}r = 23{:}1$$

Another way to write this is

$$11/r = 23/1$$

23/1 is just 23, so I can write:

$$\frac{11}{r} = 23$$

There is a way to solve this equation using the triangle method. You're familiar with the triangle being used when the equation contains three symbols, but it works just as well when the equation is a mixture of numbers and symbols, as in this equation.

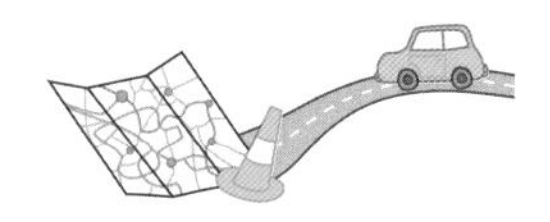

The triangle that's appropriate here is shown in Figure 12.

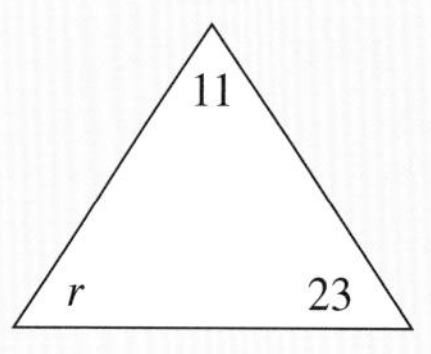

Figure 12 A triangle to solve the equation $11/r = 23$

You can use the triangle in Figure 12 to write the equation:

$$r = \frac{11}{23}$$

which works out to $r = 0.48$ (to two significant figures).

We have seen that transmitting an image of just the number plate instead of the whole frame gives a useful reduction of data rate, with the old and new data rates in the ratio of 23:1. Can anything further be done to reduce the data rate?

One possibility is compression. This could be used whether a whole picture is sent per car or whether only a picture of the number plate is sent. Lossy compression (for example the JPEG process) would be most suitable for photographic images such as these. The amount of compression that could be achieved depends on the nature of the image and the amount of degradation that can be tolerated. However, compression ratios of the order of 30:1 are quite typical. Note, though, that compressing an image requires further processing, so the reduction of data rate comes at the price of having to do more processing at the roadside cabinet.

Compression may not be the only way to get further reductions in the data rate. Suppose that the number plate images are analysed at the roadside cabinet in order to identify the letters and numbers in the number plates. Instead of sending a picture of the car, or a picture of the number plate, codes could be sent for the letters and numbers in the number plate. Does this produce a worthwhile reduction of data rate? We will look at this in the next activity.

Activity 19 (self-assessment)

Suppose each character of a number plate is represented by an 8-bit code and that, on average, each number plate has seven characters. What data rate is now required to send number plate data to the central computer for six cars per second? (Assume that it is unnecessary to represent the space between groups of numbers and letters.)

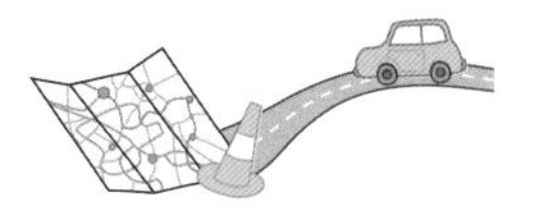

Comment

The answer is given at the end of this part.

Activity 20 (self-assessment)

What is the ratio of the data rates needed for sending an image of the number plate and for sending codes for the characters?

Comment

The answer is given at the end of this part.

From the preceding activities you can see that if no processing is carried out at the roadside cabinet, the data rate would be very high with six cars per second passing.

If the image to be transmitted could be restricted to just the number plate alone, rather than the whole image, then data rates fall dramatically, though a broadband link might still be needed. If the image is compressed (either the whole image or just the number plate), the data rate is reduced although further processing is required.

If character recognition is done at the roadside, so that just the codes for the characters on the number plates need to be sent, the data rate would be very low, allowing the use of the lowest bandwidth links (such as a standard telephone link at 64 kbit/s).

It looks, then, as though there are choices to be made between doing no processing at the roadside, or doing varying amounts of processing. If no processing is done at the roadside, the high data rate might need expensive new cabling, for example optical fibres. If some processing were done, for example just sending pictures of the number plates, existing telephone lines might be used as broadband links. If a lot of processing were done at the roadside, the data link might be very cheap. However, processing data at the roadside raises the cost of the roadside installations, besides making them more complex and possibly more likely to be out of action for part of the time.

As so often in technological design, a choice has to be made between various options, each of which has advantages and drawbacks. You will recall that when the Central London Congestion Charging scheme was set up, all the data (in the form of analogue video images) was transmitted over optical fibre for analysis centrally. Evidently this was judged worthwhile for the relatively small area used in the London scheme, but could be problematic for a scheme covering a much bigger area.

I should introduce a note of caution here. The calculations you have just done were based on very simple models. In digital data transmission, the original data nearly always needs to be augmented with additional data at the transmitting end to enable it to be recovered reliably at the

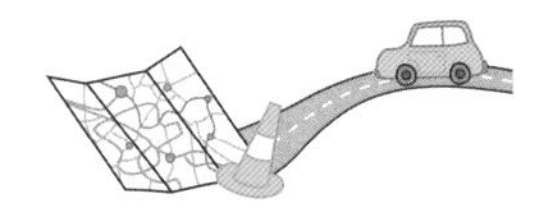

receiver. However, simple calculations such as the ones performed in the activities above are useful for exploring the implications of different scenarios.

4.6 Other methods and other uses

In the last subsection we looked at using ANPR as a way of identifying cars for road-charging schemes, but there are other techniques that could be used. (Some techniques have already been mentioned, but there are further possibilities.)

Activity 21 (exploratory)

What other techniques or technologies that you are familiar with or have met in your studies do you think could be used to identify a vehicle or a vehicle's driver without the vehicle needing to stop?

Comment

An RFID tag could be attached to a vehicle. RFID relies upon radio frequencies to relay information held on the tag, so this could be an effective method. It would, however, be necessary to ensure that the identity could not be changed in order to defraud a charging scheme, should it be used for this purpose.

My mobile telephone uses a form of smart card to identify it to the mobile network. However, possessing a mobile phone in itself does not identify the person or the vehicle because it could be stolen or borrowed by others.

Various active techniques are possible, in which the car has a transmitter of some kind that sends out an identifying signal.

Identification techniques such as ANPR and the others mentioned in Activity 21 could be applied to vehicles for purposes other than road charging.

Activity 22 (exploratory)

For what other purposes could identification techniques be applied to vehicles?

Comment

One possibility is to identify motorists who travel at persistently higher speeds than permitted between monitoring points on a motorway. (Section 4.7 looks at how this could be done.)

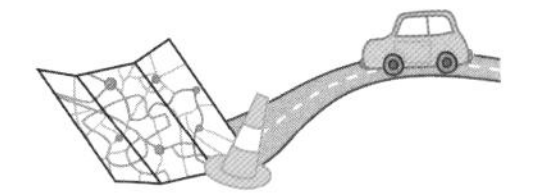

Identification methods could also be used to identify vehicles that are authorised to park in areas where parking is restricted.

Another possibility is tracing untaxed or stolen vehicles (if the scheme covers a big enough area). A database of stolen vehicles could be maintained, and all cars identified in a particular identification scheme could be checked against it.

4.7 Timing vehicles

Activity 22 mentioned that identification techniques such as ANPR could allow the speed of vehicles to be monitored. This information could be used by a control centre as an indication of the degree of congestion on parts of a road network. A system using ANPR is used on most of the major roads in the UK for just this purpose.

To see how the system works, suppose a vehicle is logged as it passes camera A, and logged again as it passes camera B some distance further along the road (Figure 13).

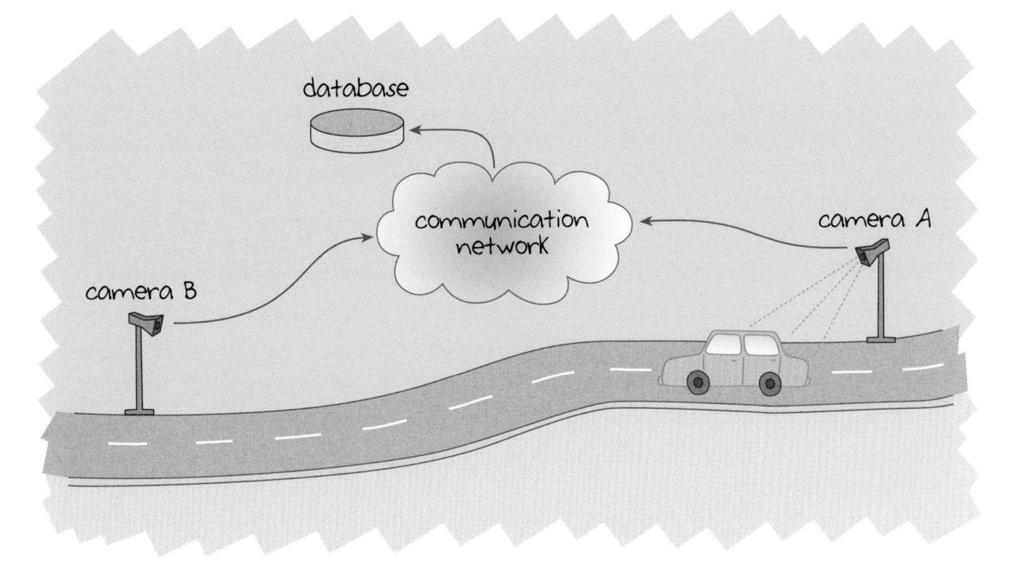

Figure 13 Using ANPR for timing a vehicle as it passes two points

Data from the two cameras can be compared. The elapsed time between the car passing A and B is an effective indicator of the average speed of the vehicle between the cameras. Knowing the distance between the monitoring points, the average speed can be calculated for each vehicle if necessary.

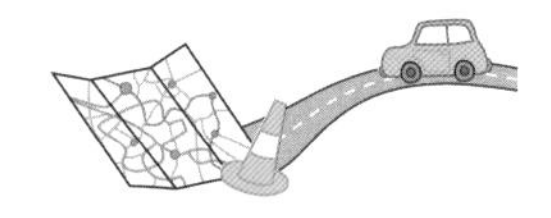

In the next activity I shall ask you to use times expressed in mixed units of hours, minutes and seconds. These can be tricky to work out. Your calculator may have a function to help here, but if it hasn't then one way to work out the lapsed time would be to convert the times expressed in hours, minutes and seconds into seconds only. Subtracting one time in seconds from the other time in seconds is then straightforward.

Activity 23 (self-assessment)

A car passes one monitoring point at a time of 10:33:05 a.m. (read this as 10 hours, 33 minutes and 5 seconds) and the same car passes the next monitoring point at 11:05:25 a.m. on the same day.

(a) What is the average speed (expressed in km/hour) of the car between these two points, given that they are separated by 10 km?

(b) Could you assume that this data gives a reliable indication of the time needed to travel between these two points?

Comment

The answer is given at the end of this part.

The sort of data used in the last activity, where individual vehicles are identified and their speed calculated, could be used to catch speeding motorists. There is an issue here about information being collected by commercial organisations for one purpose (for example to provide information to drivers) potentially being used for another purpose (the detection by police of motoring offences or criminal activity). The legal position can vary between countries. In the UK, at the time of writing, data about individual cars from commercially collected traffic data is not routinely disclosed to outside bodies, though exceptional circumstances may cause this to change.

4.8 Summary of Section 4

Three main types of road charging are in use or have been proposed: zone charging, tolls and road charging (which is charging by the amount of use made of the road network).

Charging for network use depends on being able to identify users and monitor their detailed use of the network. In the case of road charging by zone or toll, this means identifying vehicles and registering their presence on a road link or in a particular district.

Automatic number plate recognition (ANPR) is a suitable technology for road charging by zone or toll. It brings together shape analysis, character recognition and data transmission technologies.

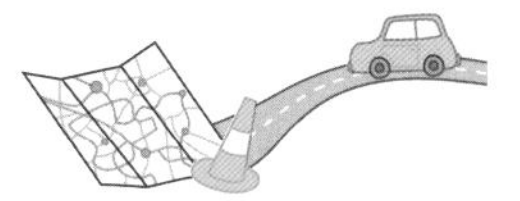

Practical schemes require decisions to be made about the extent to which data analysis is done at the monitoring point and the extent to which it is done centrally. If data analysis were done at the monitoring point, the data rates needed for transmission to the central computer could be very low. However, this increases the cost of each monitoring point. If data analysis were done centrally, monitoring points could be relatively cheap, but data rates would be higher, and might need special links.

Identification techniques such as ANPR can be used for monitoring car speeds and congestion.

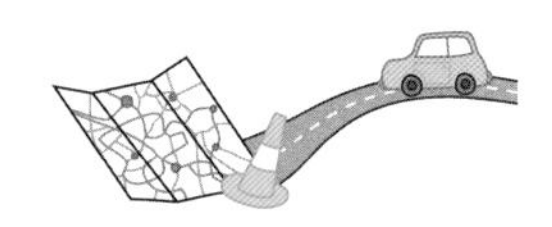

5 Tracking technology

5.1 Tracking and road charging

Mention was made earlier of road charging by the distance driven, which has attracted the interest of several governments. It is seen as a practical option for managing road networks and for bringing road congestion under control.

In a sense, charging by the distance driven already exists, through a driver's fuel expenditure. The further a vehicle travels, the more the driver has to pay, and the more revenue a government gets from fuel taxation. The proposed charging-by-distance schemes, however, offer much finer control of the network than is possible with control by fuel expenditure. The key to charging by distance over a wide area is *variable* charging. Different roads could have different charging rates; and different stretches of the same road could have different rates. Charges could also vary according to the time of day or year.

Besides offering much finer network management, charging by distance is seen as potentially fairer to the road haulage industry. For instance, at the time of writing, taxation on lorries is higher in the UK than in some other countries. Consequently, hauliers based in the UK pay more for the use of UK roads through taxation than do hauliers from some other countries who also make use of UK roads. Road charging by distance could apply to all road users, irrespective of their country of origin.

As with zone charging, the proposed schemes need to be able to identify the vehicle and the person to be charged. It is also necessary to record which road a vehicle is on at any time, and how far along the road the vehicle travels – so that the appropriate charge can be applied. Until relatively recently, doing this over an area the size of a country (or a continent) would have been impractical. Now, however, ICTs are starting to make such schemes look feasible. However, the practicalities of making such a system work are quite formidable. Data about the vehicle and its movements needs to be relayed from almost anywhere on the road system to a central processing system and analysed, so that itemised bills can be sent to the driver or owner of the vehicle. This could amount to a lot of data traffic.

Accurate tracking of vehicles is clearly essential for charging by distance to work. However, ANPR is not really practical as a tracking method for a truly nationwide scheme. Consider, for instance, a major road with ANPR cameras located every few kilometres along it (as they currently are on many major roads). A vehicle could be logged as it passed the cameras, and the distance travelled deduced from the locations of all the cameras that logged the vehicle. But suppose the vehicle left the main road and drove for several miles along minor roads before rejoining the major road. Unless all the minor roads also had ANPR cameras, the total

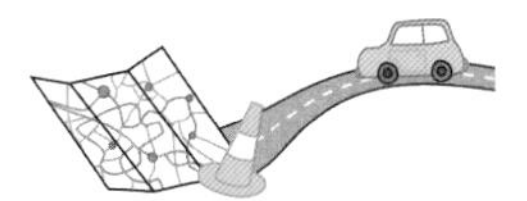

distance travelled could not be accurately calculated. Putting ANPR cameras on all roads in many countries is hardly practical.

Figure 14 presents one approach for a wide-area charging-by-distance scheme, which I will now explain. All vehicles carry a small on-board unit. The on-board unit has a satellite receiver which can work out the position of the vehicle using the Global Positioning System (GPS), which I will say more about shortly. A record of the vehicle's movements is kept in the on-board unit. The on-board unit also has a charging map of the area where the vehicle is being driven, so that the driver can know what charges are being accumulated. The on-board unit could also, in theory, keep a record of the speed the vehicle was driven at.

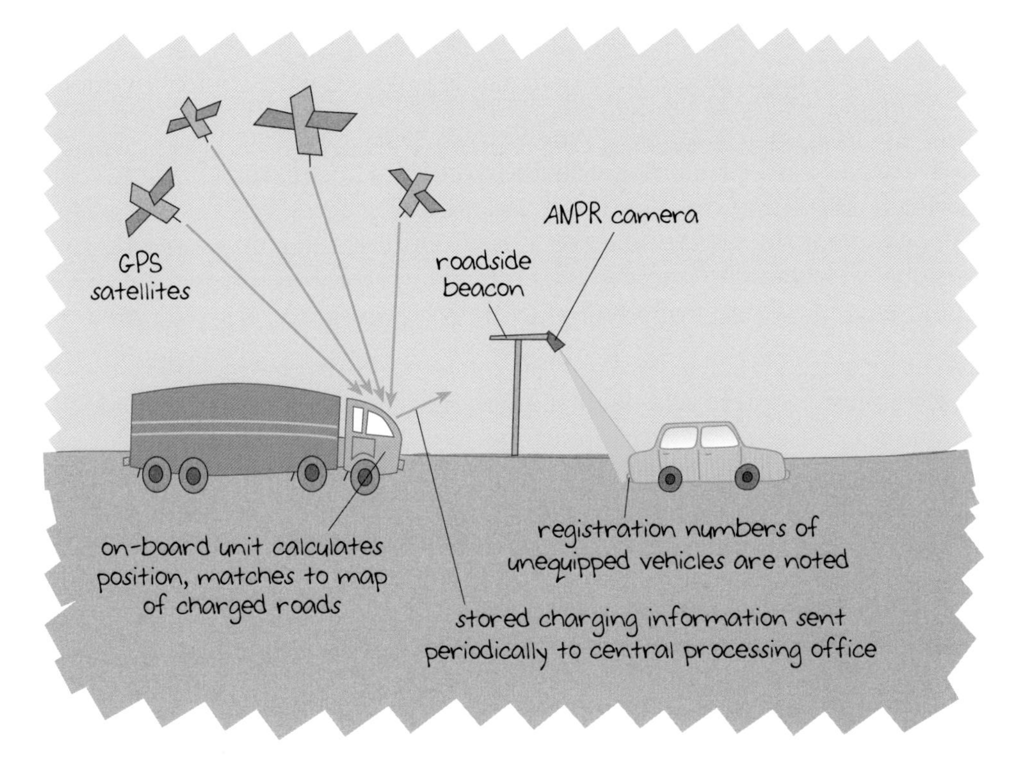

Figure 14 Proposed vehicle tracking for road charging

Periodically a record of the vehicle's movements must be uploaded to the charging system. There are several ways in which this might happen, and more might be devised. One possibility is for the on-board unit to communicate with a roadside beacon, sending details of itself (so that the vehicle and its keeper can be identified) and details of the journey driven since the last communication. This data would then be relayed from the roadside beacon to the central processing facility so that itemised bills could be sent to the appropriate person. (Various payment systems would be possible, such as direct debit of a person's account for use of the road.) The beacon incorporates an ANPR camera so that vehicles without an on-board unit could be identified. These might be rogue road users, but might also be legitimate road users without on-board units, for instance foreign vehicles visiting the country. It is

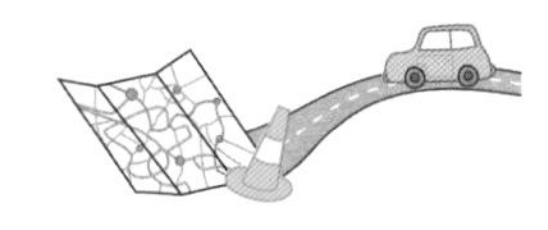

possible that a system other than ANPR could be used here. For instance, there might be an internationally agreed system of vehicle tagging enabling vehicles to be identified by roadside monitors. The essential point is that vehicles using the road but incapable of being identified in the usual way need to be recognised.

The EC plans for all new vehicles from 2009 to be fitted with equipment for making automatic 'eCalls' to emergency services in the event of an accident. The eCall will identify the location automatically.

Various techniques for communicating data from cars to beacons have been proposed. One is to use a mobile wireless data-networking system called Dedicated Short Range Communications (DSRC), which operates on microwaves. This system is still in development at the time of writing, and could be used for many other things than for road charging (in fact, road charging is not the principal use envisaged by its developers). I will say more about DSRC later.

Another proposal is to upload data from the car to the central processing facility via the mobile phone system rather than via the roadside beacon. Yet another possibility is to transfer data via a smartcard (a card containing a memory chip). The smartcard would normally live in the on-board unit and would store details of road use. At convenient stops (for example, filling stations) the card would be run through a card reader and the data transmitted for processing. The driver might have the option of paying for the road use along with the fuel.

As for locating vehicles, so that their movements can be recorded, the mobile phone system has been suggested as an alternative to satellite positioning. (The cellular nature of the mobile phone system enables an approximate fix on a mobile phone's position to be achieved.) However, satellite positioning offers much more accurate fixing of a vehicle's position, so I will say a little about how it works.

5.2 Global Positioning System (GPS)

In this section I will look at how it is possible to fix the position of a receiver using the **Global Positioning System (GPS)**.

Global Positioning System (GPS)

Activity 24 (self-assessment)

An introduction to GPS is presented on the T175 DVD; it introduces important ideas that underpin the operation of GPS. Run this animation, and then write a short explanation (about 150 words) of how the GPS system enables a receiver's location to be determined.

Comment

My answer is given at the end of this part.

In practice, the process is much more sophisticated and detailed than I have suggested. For instance, as well as measuring the propagation time very precisely, it is also necessary to include any changes in the

propagation speed for a radio wave's path (for example, as it enters the Earth's atmosphere).

Another requirement is to know accurately the positions of each participating satellite at the time of measurement. The satellites that are used are not geostationary and so move continuously in relation to the Earth. Other physical effects also have to be taken into account.

Activity 25 (self-assessment)

Popular journalism often refers to satellites surveying or 'tracking' the movements of individuals or vehicles. Briefly summarise why this is wrong in the context of GPS.

Comment

The answer is given at the end of this part.

I shall now describe the processes involved in the measurement of the propagation time. This will show that the location we get from the simple three-satellite triangulation is not really as accurate as we need for many purposes. This is the reason that four satellites are used.

The signal that is transmitted from a satellite to a GPS receiver contains a sequence of code that runs continuously and synchronously (in step) at both the GPS receiver and the GPS satellite transmitter. Figure 15 indicates the nature of the coded signal.

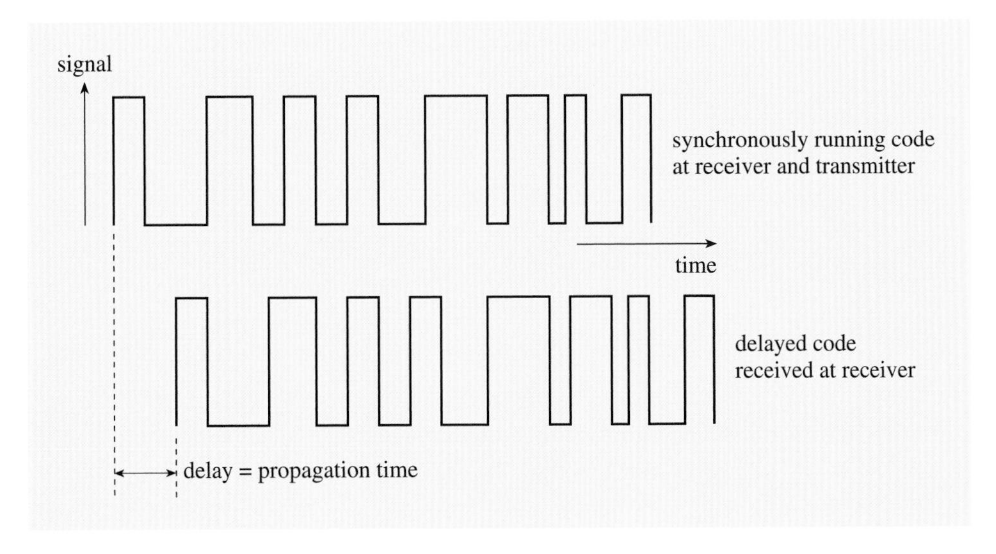

Figure 15 GPS code

The code (called a pseudo-binary random sequence) has some special properties and advantages which make it easier to detect the very weak signals reliably at the GPS receiver on the ground. The receiver therefore does not need a large antenna, which would otherwise be needed for such weak signals.

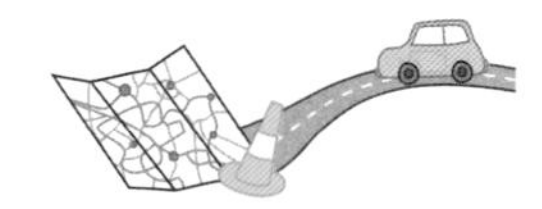

Assuming that the code sequence runs in perfect synchronism at both the transmitter and the receiver, the GPS receiver can compare the received code with the code already running at the receiver. The received code will appear delayed by the amount of time that it has taken to propagate from the transmitter – that is, it will appear to have been shifted in time (see Figure 15). The adjustment in time needed to bring the received and the receiver code sequences back into alignment is the time it takes for the signal to travel from the satellite transmitter to the receiver.

I shall now carry out an example calculation to estimate the time taken for a signal to reach the Earth's surface from a GPS satellite directly above, at an altitude of 20 200 km. You should recall that a radio signal travels at the speed of light, which is approximately 3×10^8 m/s. I will assume that the velocity of the signal is unchanged over the whole path length.

From Figure 16:

$$\text{Time} = \text{distance}/\text{velocity}$$

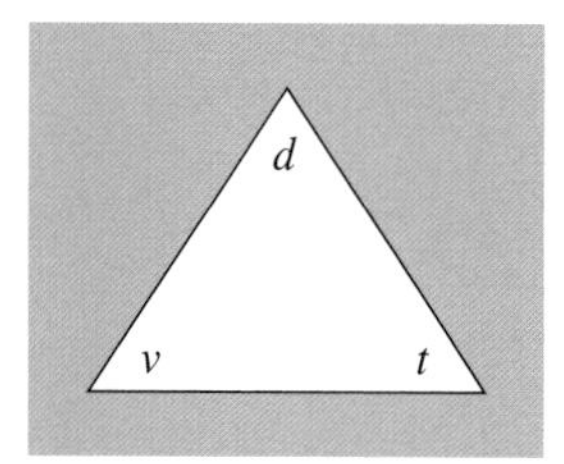

Figure 16 Triangle illustrating the relationship between time(t), distance (d) and velocity (v)

The first step is to ensure that all units of measurement are compatible with each other. In this example, I need to convert kilometres into metres:

$$20\ 200 \text{ km} = 20\ 200\ 000 \text{ m} = 2.02 \times 10^7 \text{ m}$$

My calculation then becomes:

$$\frac{2.02 \times 10^7}{3 \times 10^8}$$

To simplify the calculation, I will use the 'shortcut' for calculating the results of dividing one number by another number when expressed in scientific notation. You should recall that this was introduced earlier in the course and showed that the calculation above becomes:

$$\frac{2.02}{3} \times 10^{(7-8)} \text{ s} = 0.67 \times 10^{-1} \text{ s}$$

But how should we interpret the negative exponent ($^{-1}$) in 10^{-1}? In fact, 10^{-1} means 1/10, or 0.1, as the box 'Negative exponents' explains.

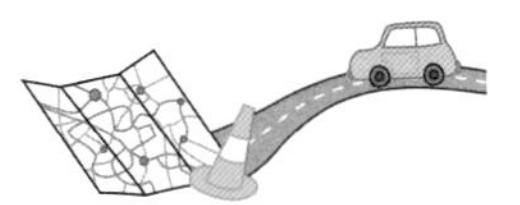

Negative exponents

We can appreciate what negative exponents mean by looking at the pattern of positive exponents in Table 5. On the left, the 'Powers of 10' column shows a series of tens with exponents decreasing by step from 4 to 0. The middle column shows what the numbers in the 'Powers of 10' column are equivalent to as a series of multiplications. The result of these multiplications appears in the right-hand column in 'Ordinary notation'.

Table 5 Sequence of positive powers of ten

Powers of 10	Equivalent to	Ordinary notation
10^4	$= 10 \times 10 \times 10 \times 10$	= 10 000 (ten thousand)
10^3	$= 10 \times 10 \times 10$	= 1000 (one thousand)
10^2	$= 10 \times 10$	= 100 (one hundred)
10^1	$= 10$	= 10 (ten)
10^0	$= 1$	= 1 (one)

Notice how, as you move down through the rows, the effect of reducing the exponent by 1 is to reduce the result of the calculation by a factor of 10.

Table 6 extends this series to negative exponents. Again, the effect of reducing the exponent by 1 is to reduce the result of the calculation by a factor of 10.

Table 6 Sequence of negative powers of ten

Powers of 10	Equivalent to	Ordinary notation
10^0	$= 1$	= 1 (one)
10^{-1}	$= \frac{1}{10}$	= 0.1 (one-tenth)
10^{-2}	$= \frac{1}{10 \times 10}$	= 0.01 (one-hundredth)
10^{-3}	$= \frac{1}{10 \times 10 \times 10}$	= 0.001 (one-thousandth)
10^{-4}	$= \frac{1}{10 \times 10 \times 10 \times 10}$	= 0.0001 (one ten-thousandth)

If you compare positive and negative exponents you should notice a relationship between them. For example, $10^2 = 100$ and $10^{-2} = 1/100$. The negative exponent turns a number into the inverse or **reciprocal** of the number created by the corresponding positive exponent.

reciprocal

Below are three examples of conversion from scientific notation with negative exponents into ordinary notation. Notice how the

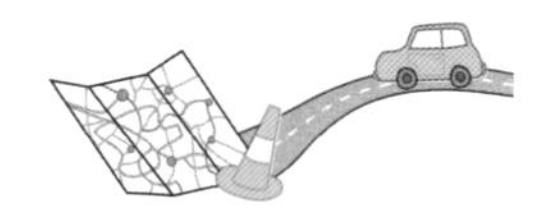

answer can be obtained by moving the decimal point in the scientific notation to the left by a number of steps equal to the number in the exponent.

2.73×10^{-1} is 0.273 (decimal point moved 1 place to the left)

4.5×10^{-4} is 0.00045 (decimal point moved 4 places to the left)

7×10^{-6} is 0.000007 (decimal point moved 6 places to the left)

In the last example I had to start by inserting a decimal point after the 7.

Returning to our answer for the time taken for a signal to travel from the GPS satellite to the Earth, we had the following value:

0.67×10^{-1} s

The negative exponent tells us that if we want to express this in ordinary notation, we move the decimal point one place to the left. That is, 0.067 s.

Activity 26 (self-assessment)

Taking the speed of the radio signal as 3×10^{8} m/s, calculate the time taken for a signal to reach the Earth's surface from a GPS satellite at a position 19 400 km distant from the GPS receiver. Assume that the velocity is unchanged over the whole path length.

Comment

The answer is given at the end of this part

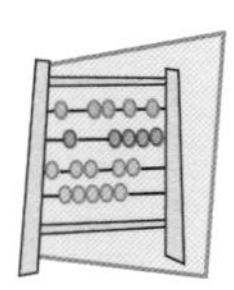

Activity 27 (self-assessment)

Suppose that for the location of a vehicle to be determined sufficiently accurately, the distance from a satellite needed to be accurate to within 1 m. What level of timing precision would be needed? (Hint: Calculating the time for a radio wave to propagate over a distance of 1 m will give an indication of this.)

Comment

The answer is given at the end of this part.

The last two activities suggest that GPS needs to measure a time delay of somewhere around 60 or 70 ms to a precision of about 3 ns for a resolution of 1 metre to be achieved. For military purposes, resolutions of the order of 1 cm are possible, but require corresponding increases in timing precision.

High-accuracy atomic clocks are available, but they are expensive. The cost of such a clock can be justified on a GPS satellite (of which there are only 24), but not in a low-cost GPS receiver (of which there are many). The clocks in GPS receivers are not sufficiently accurate to identify a precise location from three satellites. A solution to this problem lies in using a fourth satellite. A fourth satellite enables the major potential errors in timing to be corrected for, as I shall now explain.

If we think of the lines joining the GPS receiver to three satellites that the receiver is using, in a perfectly accurate system the three lines will meet in a single point. If any or all of the time measurements are inaccurate, then the intersection is likely to be ill defined, like a large fuzzy ball of cotton wool rather than a single point. The true location is somewhere within the fuzzy ball, but without more information the location cannot be pinned down more precisely. This is where the fourth satellite comes in.

If all the timings (and the corresponding distances) were absolutely precise, then a fourth satellite measurement should coincide precisely with the single point of intersection from the other three. In the real, imprecise world, the fourth measurement allows a timing correction to be computed. The correction can then be applied to the GPS receiver's clock, ensuring it falls into line with the superior satellite atomic clocks on board the GPS satellites. So the fourth satellite reading allows the lower-quality receiver clocks to become synchronised with the atomic clocks in the satellites.

However, even with the correction produced by the fourth satellite, there is uncertainty whether the accuracy obtained with the GPS system is good enough for a road-charging system. According to the Department for Transport (2005).

> ... existing systems [i.e. the GPS system] can give a vehicle's position as being in the middle of a building rather than on a road alongside it. This may not matter for normal navigation or tracking needs, where software (often referred to as 'snap to map') can correct this error, by assuming that the vehicle must be on the road. But the assumption may be wrong – the software may correct the vehicle's position to the wrong road. If the charges on the two roads are different, the vehicle may be wrongly charged.
>
> Department for Transport (2005), p. 22

At the time of writing, the accuracy of the original GPS system, for civilian use, was in the hands of the American government. The system was designed for military use, and for that purpose gives extremely accurate location data. For civilian use, the accuracy is deliberately degraded. The European Galileo system of navigation satellites, due to

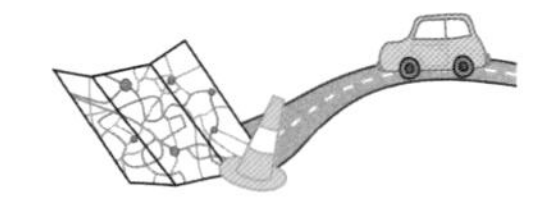

be operational in 2008, is expected to give better accuracy for civilian applications.

As for when a national charging-by-distance scheme might be operational in the UK, the Department for Transport (2005) says:

> National road pricing is thus not currently technologically feasible in terms of practicality, functionality and cost. But it is becoming so. Our best estimate is that it will be available within the next 10 to 15 years. This view is based on market-led development of satellite navigation and the deployment over the coming years of the Galileo satellites leading to more accurate and reliable equipment. Prices are falling. Satellite navigation systems are set to become standard fitting on mainstream popular cars within a few years, and insurance companies are also interested in the possibilities they offer for pay-as-you-go policies.
>
> Department for Transport (2005), p. 43

5.3 Avoiding the traffic: Smartnav

Although the accuracy of the GPS system may be in doubt for a large-scale road-charging scheme, its accuracy is good enough for motorists' and sailors' navigational aids. At the time of writing GPS devices are fairly widely used for navigational aids in vehicles. 'Smartnav' is one example. It is an 'intelligent' navigation service provided by TrafficMaster plc, a company with its headquarters in Cranfield, Bedfordshire, UK.

Subscribers to Smartnav have an on-board unit installed in their cars, which tells the driver (in a synthesised voice) which way to turn at road junctions. The unit's instructions take account of current traffic conditions, directing the driver around hold-ups if there are any ahead. The arrangement of the ICT networks involved is indicated in Figure 17.

The on-board unit has a GPS receiver and a link to the control centre via a mobile phone network. To use the system the driver alerts the control centre by pressing a button on the dashboard (or elsewhere) to speak to a human adviser. The driver informs the adviser of the required destination, and the vehicle's current location is transmitted to the computer in the control centre via the mobile signal. The computer plots a route, which is sent to the on-board unit via the mobile phone link.

TrafficMaster uses a network of infrared ANPR cameras along major roads in the UK. Data from these and other sources enables the Smartnav control centre to maintain a database of the current state of traffic flow on most of the major roads and motorways in the UK. (Section 4.7 explained how data from ANPR cameras could be used to monitor the average speed of vehicles on a stretch of road.) The route that is sent to the Smartnav subscriber takes account of prevailing traffic conditions.

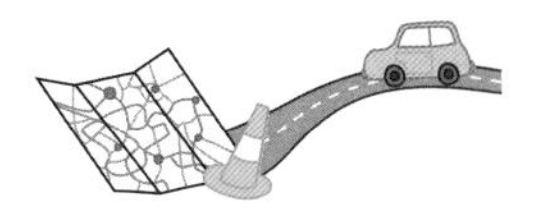

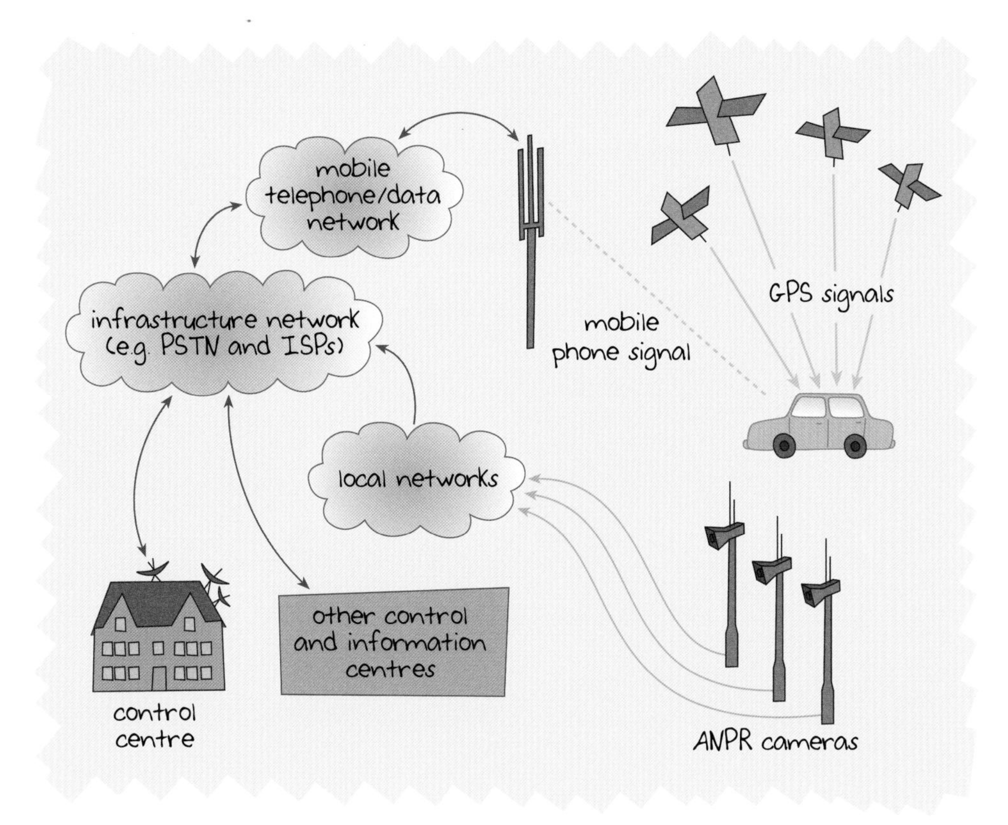

Figure 17 Smartnav

As the subscriber drives along the route that has been sent from the control centre, the on-board GPS receiver monitors the car's position so that appropriate instructions can be given. Modifications to the route can be issued during the journey if, for instance, the driver misses a turning.

5.4 Summary of Section 5

Nationwide road-charging systems are being contemplated by many countries. Generally they involve vehicle tracking. Navigation satellites and on-board GPS units would provide a method of self-location by vehicles. Vehicle details and journey information would be relayed to roadside monitoring points, or to other static data collectors.

The GPS system enables a receiver to establish its location from signals received from four satellites. Timing information derived from the signals enable the distance to each satellite to be calculated. Theoretically, data from three satellites should be all that is required. A fourth satellite enables inaccuracies due to timing imperfections in the receiver to be overcome. Even so, the result might be too inaccurate for road charging in some locations. The European Galileo system is expected to provide the accuracy needed for a road-charging scheme.

Satellite navigation systems can also be used for in-car navigation aids.

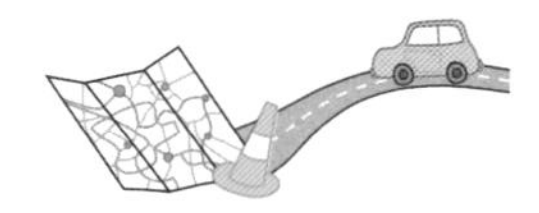

6 Smarter vehicles

6.1 DSRC networks

Dedicated Short-Range Communication (DSRC) networks have already been mentioned in connection with road-charging schemes as a possible way for vehicles to transfer journey details to roadside receivers. However, DSRC networks are envisaged for much more than that.

ad hoc network
The Latin term 'ad hoc' is used to mean 'for a particular purpose'

DSRC is under development at the time of writing, although prototypes have been tested. Vehicles equipped with DSRC equipment can form temporary, or ad hoc, wireless networks with other DSRC-equipped vehicles nearby. Figure 18 shows such an **ad hoc network** between vehicles A and B.

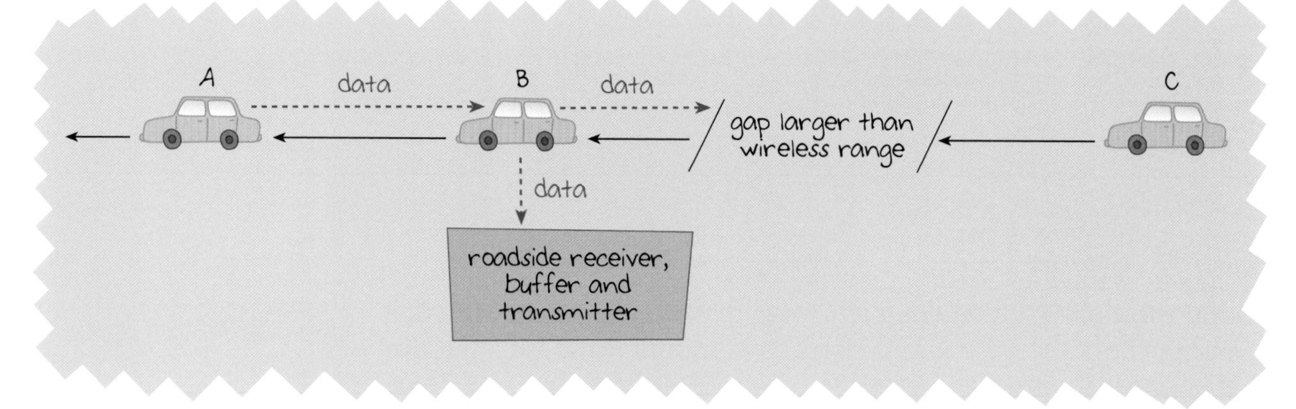

Figure 18 Formation of an ad hoc network between cars

These wireless networks would be created spontaneously as vehicles encountered each other. Roadside receivers are also incorporated into networks in the vicinity of vehicles A and B, as shown in Figure 18.

Each vehicle in the network can act as a sender, router or receiver of information, and the range of each vehicle's transmitter would be around 1 km, depending on the terrain and the environment. Out-of-range vehicles, such as C in Figure 18, are not part of the network, although they could be part of other networks.

Many types of information could be relayed between the vehicles. For instance, a vehicle encountering fog, ice, congestion or an accident could automatically inform all road users in the area. The roadside receiver could save this information for the benefit of other vehicles such as C as they come into range.

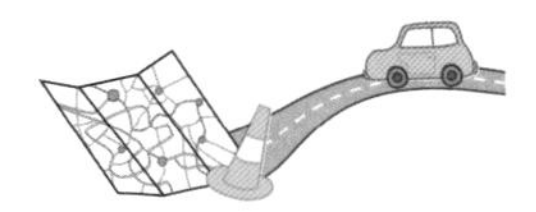

The potential applications of DSRC are still being explored at the time of writing. One proposal is a 'merging assistant':

> ... as you drive along the sliproad onto the motorway, you enter a cooperative scenario where your vehicle negotiates with other vehicles on the motorway. [...] 'Such a system might advise you of the right speed to drive at to merge smoothly with the existing traffic or, potentially, the cars on the road could move apart to make a gap for you to fit into.'
>
> Evans-Pughe (2005), p. 43–44

Another proposal is that vehicles could communicate their braking behaviour to other vehicles so that, for instance, a car executing an emergency stop can inform the vehicles behind. These following vehicles could automatically execute emergency stops immediately their drivers press the brake pedal.

Another proposal is to use DSRC in conjunction with on-board radar:

> Cambridge Consultants (CCL) has developed a way to combine 5.8 GHz DSRC communications with its 5.8 GHz Softcar radar system using shared transmitters and receiver antennas. [...]
>
> A car equipped with the CCL system would be able to identify the exact position and speed of a maximum of eight other vehicles by using calculations based on the radar measurements.
>
> [In Figure 19] a Softcar radar system in our car registers the presence and relative positions of the three vehicles in front. At the same time, DSRC communications from the overhead gantry convey details of lane-specific speed limits. The orange car directly in front communicates that it is slowing down and the blue car to the right communicates that it is executing an emergency stop – in both instances via DSRC. Our car, using positional information derived from the Softcar system, knows that it does not need to execute an emergency stop since it is in a different lane from the blue car.
>
> Evans-Pughe (2005), p. 46

As you can see from these examples, DSRC is not just envisaged as a means of communication; it is also envisaged as a resource for increasingly autonomous vehicles – that is, vehicles that take over some of the driver's functions. Such developments are likely to raise anxieties or opposition, which I will discuss further in Section 6.3, but there could be powerful arguments in their favour. For instance, taking control of some processes away from the driver might make road transport safer. The Automatic Braking System (ABS), in which the car takes over some control of the brakes during emergency braking to prevent the wheels locking, is already well established. Another example is adaptive cruise control, available on some cars at the time of writing. This enables the

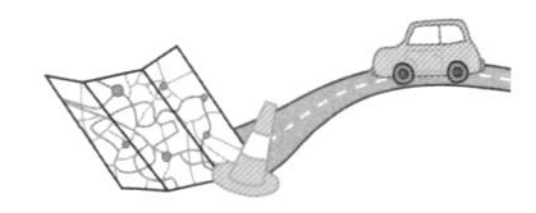

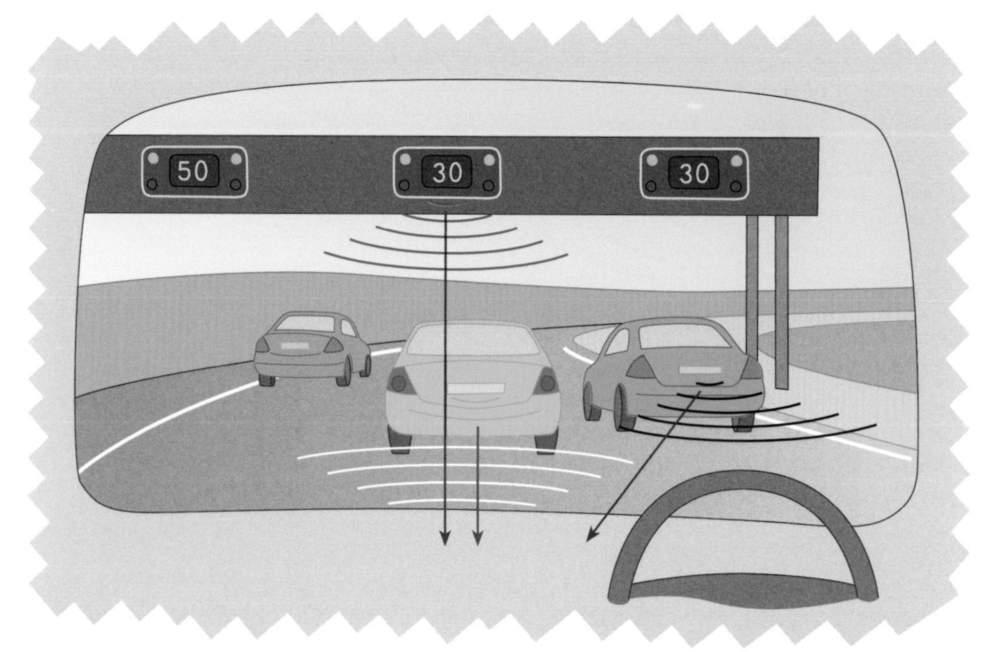

Figure 19 Softcar radar system (redrawn from Evans–Pughe, 2005)

driver to set a cruising speed, and the car monitors the distance from the car in front by radar or laser. If the distance gets too short, or if another vehicles cuts in, the cruise-controlled vehicle slows down automatically. If the gap widens and the vehicle is travelling at less than its cruising speed, it accelerates.

6.2 On-board networks

Modern vehicles almost universally use on-board computers and ICT networks to monitor and control at least some aspects of engine performance and exhaust emissions. In some vehicles, network control is extended to include transmission and braking systems, ventilation, cruise control and so on.

Within a vehicle, communication occurs over what is in effect, a Local Area Network (LAN), but is termed a Controller Area Network (CAN). There are standards specifying protocols for CANs in vehicles, just as there are for networks that are used for other purposes.

drive-by-wire

One application of networks in cars is so-called **drive-by-wire** systems. These replace mechanical linkages with short-range network links. For example, replacing a steering column by a drive-by-wire or at least a steer-by-wire link means that the potentially dangerous mechanical steering column between the steering wheel and the road wheels is replaced by a communication link with appropriate sensors and actuators at either end of it. A mechanical steering column can be a life-threatening feature in a collision.

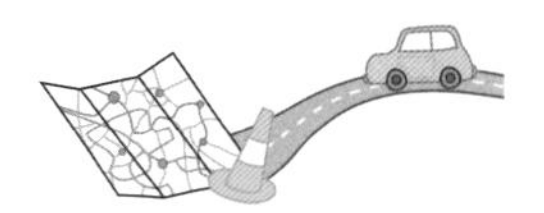

Further examples of communication networks within vehicles are given by integrated in-vehicle entertainment systems and internet connectivity. These are increasingly being offered in new vehicles. What will these mean for drivers in practice? That is hard to say, but some facilities may not be as futuristic as they appear. Everything in the box 'Another week begins' can be found in vehicles as I write in 2005.

Another week begins

It's 8 a.m. on a Monday morning. I open my car door to start my day's travels. The internal SIM card in my integrated mobile phone and PDA identifies me as a legitimate driver of the vehicle, activates the vehicle ignition and switches off the security system. My mobile phone communicates wirelessly with the on-board communication system and hands over its functionality until I (and it) next leave the car. This means that all my mobile services will be presented and controlled through my car's dashboard interface. My partner used the car over the weekend, but the mirror and driving positions are reset to my preference because the on-board system recognises my presence and can refer to my stored user profile for the settings.

I activate some additional functions by speaking to my dashboard. The speech recognition system on the on-board computer interprets my requests for heating, de-mister settings and so on. If I'd bought the next model up, the more intelligent system would have done this without any intervention from me.

After I have dropped off the children at school, I check that the on-board TV displays and games consoles have been put away, then it's time for the day's work.

I need some navigational support to reach my first client as I haven't been there before. I place the request through my on-board satellite navigation service and I receive a suggested route with necessary diversions round the traffic problems to my destination. Monday mornings are never easy.

I need to check for urgent office messages, and the communications interface indicates that I have an urgent voice mail message, which is then read out to me by a voice simulator.

The navigation system also has a voice simulator and this occasionally interrupts the radio programme that I am listening to and informs me which turn to take at each junction and roundabout. Eventually I arrive at my client's car park. The access control system checks my number plate against a record of expected visitors who have requested car parking. Good! There is a parking space reserved for me, indicated by a 'Welcome Mr Jones' display. I do hope there's a fresh coffee on offer!

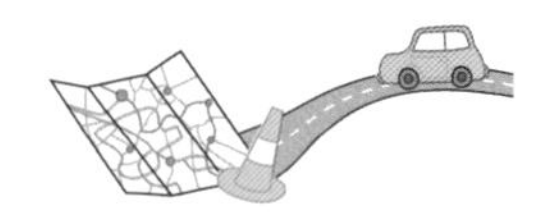

6.3 Driving the future

The scenario given in the box in the last section is typical of popular accounts of the developments possible with ICT. A world is conjured up of devices that do lots of useful tasks, and always properly (by no means guaranteed, in many people's experience). What is usually left out of these descriptions is anything contentious. But, as we probably all know from experience, life is rarely so straightforward. So, in this final section, I will raise some of the more controversial aspects relating to the topics that have been discussed in this part of Block 4.

One potentially controversial area has already been mentioned, namely the question of cars becoming to some degree autonomous. In acting autonomously, cars would not just do what is normally done by drivers but would make judgements and act on them.

Activity 28 (exploratory)

What legal issues might follow from incidents involving autonomous vehicles?

Comment

One issue relates to responsibility. Who, or what, is responsible for the consequences when a vehicle acts autonomously (or fails to act autonomously)?

An indication of the depth of concern over responsibility can be gained from the fact that one manufacturer in 2004 insisted that the anti-collision measures incorporated in their vehicles were for drivers' comfort or convenience only. This was believed to be an attempt by the manufacturer to distance themselves from the legal consequences of system failure. Difficult liability issues arise should an intelligent, anti-collision system be proven to have taken a wrong decision.

Road-charging schemes raise many other concerns. For instance, motorists who find themselves priced off the roads could see this as a loss of their personal freedom. In many parts of the UK and other countries there is little alternative to using a private car.

As we have seen, road-charging schemes can vary in complexity from relatively simple systems like the Central London Congestion Charging scheme to proposals for more complex systems for nationwide use. The more complex systems envisage vehicles being monitored so that their drivers can be charged according to which stretch of road they were on at a particular time.

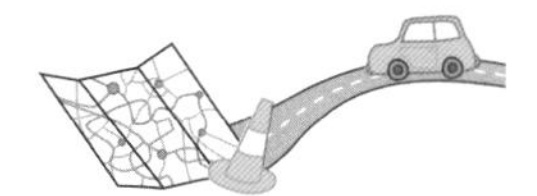

Activity 29 (exploratory)

What issue arises from the monitoring of vehicles for road-charging schemes of the type described earlier?

Comment

A major concern is whether monitoring is, in effect, surveillance. Virtually all traffic movements would be logged and recorded so that charges could be applied.

As if the question of surveillance were not cause enough for concern, there are questions over who will have access to this information about vehicle movements. Many different kinds of people might have an interest in this sort of information: the police, insurers, private detectives, managers whose staff travel as part of the job, and so on. Also, it is quite possible that a significant part of a road-charging system would be operated by, or in conjunction with, a private company which could have access to all this information about road users.

Activity 30 (exploratory)

In what ways could information about vehicle movements be useful to the police?

Comment

Information about vehicle movements could be useful in tracking stolen vehicles or get-away cars. It could also be useful for monitoring the movements of suspects. If the data about vehicle movements included speed information, that presumably would also be of interest to the police (and to insurers).

The final issue I want to mention, although there are many others, is the question of what should happen to revenue raised by a road-charging system. If such a scheme were operated in conjunction with a private company, some of the money raised would go to that company and its shareholders. Effectively, then, motorists would be paying private bodies for the privilege of using publicly constructed and maintained roads. The part of the revenue that goes to government could be used to fund improvements to transport, which might mean improving the road network, or might mean improving alternatives to road transport. On the other hand, the money might go into general government revenue for activities unrelated to transport.

During the life of this course there will almost certainly be interesting developments in the use of ICTs in all areas of road transport (and in transport generally). As a final activity, I would like you to make a quick survey of developments that have happened since this course material was prepared.

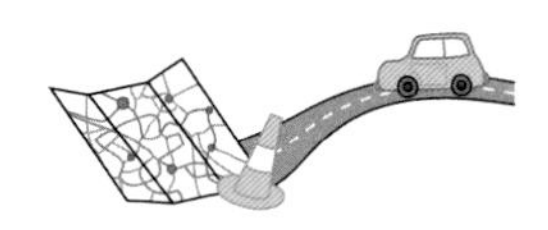

Activity 31 (exploratory)

Using a search engine, spend about 15 minutes searching for recent material relating to ICTs and transport. I suggest you search for terms such as:

road charging/road pricing

traffic congestion

DSRC

intelligent transport systems (ITS)

urban traffic management and control (UTMC)

drive-by-wire.

You will get many pages of results, but the most recent information will generally come in the first few pages. It is probably not worth going beyond the first couple of pages.

Comment

I cannot comment in detail on your findings. However, I expect that any new information you find will build upon and extend many of the ideas that I have introduced relating to the management of the road network, vehicle identification and location tracking, etc.

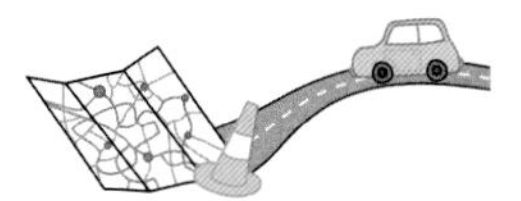

Answers to self-assessment activities

Activity 3

(a) B – from the network to the manager.

(b) C – from the network to the user.

(c) A – from the manager to the network.

In part (c) you might also have included C, because you might assume that information about the lane closure would be received by drivers. However, this was not a part of the scenario described.

Activity 4

(a) and (c) are open-loop. Once the processes are begun, there is no corrective action that can be taken if the outcome is not going to be right.

(b) and (d) are closed-loop. Corrective action can be made during the process to ensure that the right outcome is achieved.

Activity 5

The rail timetable, the coach timetable and the motoring organisation website all supplied information for planning the journey, but once the journey was under way they had no further role. This information was used in an open-loop way. The radio traffic report enabled me to modify my journey as it was happening; this use was closed-loop.

Activity 7

(a) 'Bad driving' refers to the sometimes aggressive or selfish behaviour of drivers. Drivers acting individually can destabilise formations of traffic travelling at near constant speeds. The article title would have been chosen by the author of the report rather than the originators of the computer modelling approach.

(b) Accurate and realistic models must take into account the variability of driver behaviour. Drivers in this model were characterised as being either 'aggressive' or 'defensive' in determining what could happen. The author claims that previous models did not include realistic acceleration and deceleration rates, assuming for example, that cars could stop immediately.

(c) The 'pinch effect' referred to in the article occurs during synchronised traffic flow when an individual driver's action causes others to brake. This can cause bunching, which propagates backwards.

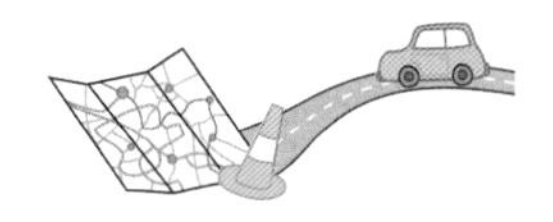

(d) Drivers take evasive action that alters the predicted outcome causing the model to be inaccurate. Schreckenberg implies that providing less than complete information to road users could actually be in everyone's best interests. Drivers who are given detailed information are more likely to react in the same way and create new problems.

Activity 9

(a) 40 vehicles per hour.

- At 20 vehicles per hour: vehicles arrive at a rate that is less than the maximum the service can cope with, so no queue will develop.
- At 30 vehicles per hour: vehicles arrive at the maximum service rate, so no queue will develop.
- At 40 vehicles per hour: the vehicles' arrival rate exceeds the maximum service rate, so a queue will develop.

(b)

- 20 vehicles per hour: any existing queue will shrink, because the arrival rate is below the maximum service rate.
- 30 vehicles per hour: the service point is operating at its maximum rate. Any existing queues will remain the same size.
- 40 vehicles per hour: existing queues will grow because the arrival rate exceeds the maximum service rate.

The above answers depend on the regularity of the service and arrivals. If service and arrivals are irregular, then the above do not necessarily remain true. You will see this for yourself shortly.

Activity 12

It is possible that variations in the arrival rate have not been taken into account. In real life, variations in the arrival rate might occur from minute to minute. Sometimes the arrival rate could be lower than the average value and at other times it could be higher. A buffer should be designed to include the effect of likely variations in the arrival rate.

Activity 15

The ones best suited to both detecting a vehicle and identifying it are the optical/video imaging and the infrared technologies. Both of these enable images containing the number plate to be obtained. The vehicle can be identified from its registration number.

The acoustic method allows particular types of vehicle to be identified, but not individual vehicles.

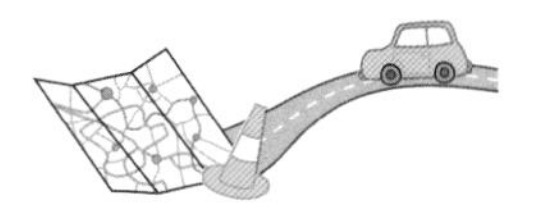

Activity 16

The number of pixels in the complete image is $768 \times 288 = 221\,184$ pixels. Each pixel can take one of 256 levels of greyness and so needs 8-bit representation ($2^8 = 256$). The total number of bits needed for a complete image frame is therefore $221\,184 \times 8$ bits $= 1\,769\,472$ bits.

Activity 17

We have seen that each image has 1 769 472 bits. As cars are passing at up to two per second in three lanes, the data rate is:

$2 \times 3 \times 1\,769\,472$ bits/s $= 11$ Mbps (to two significant figures).

Activity 18

Using a ruler I measured the dimensions of the whole image as approximately 120 mm × 45 mm, giving an area of 5400 mm^2. I then measured the dimensions of the number plate as approximately 33 mm × 7 mm, giving an area of 231 mm^2. The ratio of these two areas is:

5400:231

Dividing the numbers on either side of the ratio by 231 gives the ratio in a more convenient form:

23.3766:1, or, to two significant figures, 23:1

Another way to express this answer is to say that the area of the number plate is one twenty-third of the area of the whole picture.

Activity 19

Each character is represented by 8 bits, so seven characters require 7×8 bits $= 56$ bits. For six vehicles per second this equates to 336 bps.

Activity 20

The data rate for sending an image of the number plate was calculated earlier to be 0.48 Mbps. The data rate for sending codes for the characters was calculated in Activity 19 to be 336 bps. The ratio of these data rates is:

480 000:336

Dividing the numbers on either side of the colon by 336 gives us the more convenient form:

1430:1 (to three significant figures)

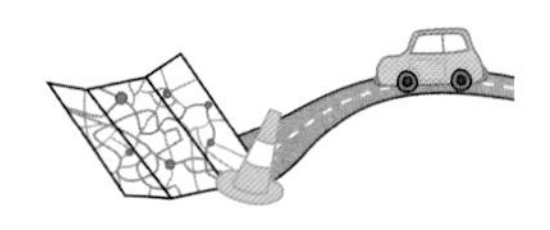

The reduction in the data rate achieved by doing the character recognition at the roadside (1430:1) is much more than can be achieved simply by compression of either the whole image or just the image of the number plate.

Activity 23

(a) First we need to find the number of seconds between 10.33.05 a.m. and 11.05.25 a.m. One way to do this is to convert each of these times to seconds, and find the difference between them.

Converting 10.33.05 into seconds:

$$10 \text{ hours} = 10 \times 60 \times 60 \text{ seconds} = 36\,000 \text{ seconds}$$

$$33 \text{ minutes} = 33 \times 60 \text{ seconds} = 1980 \text{ seconds}$$

So 10.33.05 is 36 000 + 1980 + 5 seconds after midnight. That is 37985 seconds.

Similarly, 11.05.25 can be expressed as 39 925 seconds after midnight.

The number of seconds between these two times is therefore:

$$39\,925 - 37\,985 = 1940 \text{ seconds}$$

In hours, this is:

$$1940/(60 \times 60) = 0.539 \text{ hours (to three significant figures)}$$

The average speed between the two points is given by the distance divided by the time taken, which is:

$$\frac{10 \text{ km}}{0.539 \text{ hour}} = 18.6 \text{ km per hour to three significant figures}$$

(b) The average speed is fairly low, and we would need to be careful about judging the degree of congestion from this figure. The data is historical, and so represents conditions over the previous half an hour. Traffic conditions might have changed in that time. Another concern is that the driver of the vehicle might have stopped voluntarily along the route, for example at a petrol station or for a longer period to eat. A fuller picture of conditions on that part of the network would need a lot more data relating to many more vehicles. Using more data allows a more reliable estimate of traffic congestion to be made. There are commercial organisations in the UK monitoring traffic congestion in this way. Information on traffic congestion can be sent to motoring organisations or to drivers who subscribe to the various services.

Activity 24

GPS satellites transmit radio signals that are picked up by the GPS receiver. The GPS receiver can calculate its distance from each of three satellites based on the speed of radio waves and the times taken for the waves from each satellite to reach the receiver.

For each satellite, the GPS receiver must be located somewhere on the surface of a sphere centred on the satellite, and whose radius is the calculated distance from the satellite. The intersection of the spheres from two satellites restricts the possible location of the receiver to a circle. The surface of the third sphere intersects this circle at just two points, and only one of these will be on the Earth's surface.

In theory only three satellites are needed, but to correct for timing inaccuracies in the receiver's clock, a fourth satellite is also used.

Activity 25

Global positioning satellites do not monitor the positions of receivers. Instead, receivers work out where they are from signals received from the satellites. No signals pass from the receivers up to the satellites.

Activity 26

$$\begin{aligned}\text{Time} &= \text{distance/velocity}\\ &= \frac{1.94\times10^{7}\ \text{m}}{3\times10^{8}\ \text{m/s}}\\ &= \frac{1.94}{3}\times10^{(7-8)}\ \text{s}\\ &= 0.65\times10^{-1}\ \text{s}\\ &= 0.065\ \text{s (to two significant figures)}\end{aligned}$$

In practice, the calculations would have to be far more precise than this to arrive at an accurate geographical position.

Activity 27

Time = distance/velocity. So the time for a radio wave to propagate over a distance of one metre is:

$$\frac{1}{3\times10^{8}}\ \text{s} = 3.33\times10^{-9}\ \text{s (to three significant figures)}$$

This is 3.33 nanoseconds, or 3 thousandths of a microsecond.

This gives an indication of the precision of measurement needed, based on the approximate value of the speed of light.

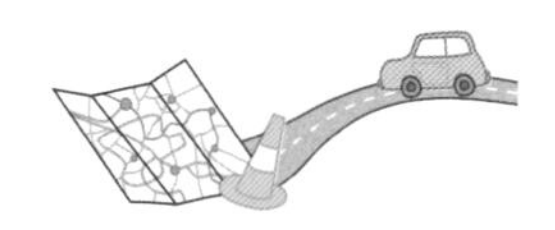

References

Department for Transport (2005) *Feasibility Study of Road Pricing in the UK*, Department for Transport.

European Commission (2001) *European Transport Policy 2010: Time To Decide*, [online] http://europa.eu.int/comm/energy_transport/library/press-kit-lben.pdf. [Accessed 6 August 2005].

Evans-Pughe, C. (2005) 'The Connected Car', *IEE Review*, January, vol. 51, no. 1, pp. 42–46.

Mullins, J. (2004) 'Bad driving holds the secret to traffic forecasts', *New Scientist*, vol. 183, no. 2454, p. 21.

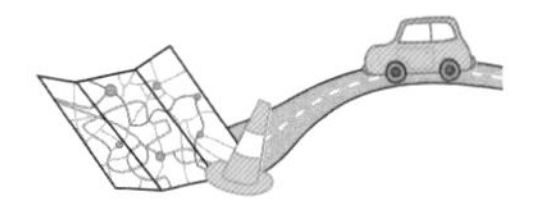

ACKNOWLEDGEMENTS

Grateful acknowledgement is made to the following sources for permission to reproduce material within this book.

Text

Mullins J., (2004), 'Bad Driving Holds the Secret to Traffic Forecasts', *New Scientist*

Figures

Figure 4: Courtesy of Variable Message Signs (VMS) Limited

Figure 19: Evans-Pughe C., (2005), 'Riding on Radar' from 'The Connected Car', *IEE Review*

Part 3
E-government

Allan Jones

1 Introduction

In many countries, e-government has become part of government policy. The UK government has a large e-government project under way, as do the governments of the USA, Australia and Japan, to name just a few. The 'e' at the start of 'e-government' stands for 'electronic', and e-government usually refers to the use by governments of ICTs. In many ways e-government is not a single activity but many activities. However, in the UK and many other countries, there is a degree of central coordination of these activities, and this is my justification for referring to e-government as though it were one project.

E-government has many aspects. For instance:

- it is an exercise in large-scale ICT project management;
- it is designed to modernise the inner workings of government;
- it is a large technical undertaking.;
- it is expensive.

Any of these could be taken as a starting point for an investigation of e-government. For this part of Block 4, however, I wish to focus on one fairly universal aim of e-government projects:

> the use of ICTs to transform the delivery of information and services to the public, and to transform how the public accesses that information.

Making information and services available on a large scale requires the extensive use of databases. I will therefore spend quite a lot of time looking at some fundamental ideas about databases. There are three reasons for devoting so much space to databases. The first reason is the importance of databases to e-government projects. Secondly, creating a database is, among other things, an analytical process. The people who specify and design a database have to think carefully about information and how it is used. In that sense, a database represents a way of thinking about information. This sort of analytical approach to information underlies almost any organised use of ICT aimed at making information available. My third reason relates to **legacy systems**. These are already installed systems, sometimes quite old, that are not designed to work together in the way their modern replacements would. In this context I shall look briefly at XML, which is a coding system widely used in e-government and elsewhere as part of the solution to legacy problems.

legacy systems

I shall also spend quite a lot of time on biometric methods of identification. These are identification methods based on fingerprints, iris patterns in the eye, and other physical characteristics. In digital form, biometric data is increasingly incorporated in, for instance, passports, driving licences and other identity documents. Identification systems, particularly ones based on biometrics, present a number of ethical, social and political issues, and I shall briefly discuss these.

E-government can hardly be successful if the public does not use it. That raises questions of usability and accessibility of the new services. I shall also be looking at some of the factors that affect usability and accessibility.

Finally, I shall look at some critical views about e-government and at proposals for using ICTs to change radically the relationship of government and public.

Throughout this part of Block 4 I draw on the writings of others. Sometimes I do this because the material I quote is authoritative or official; sometimes I do it because I think the author's view is interesting. In your own written work you will often want to draw on other sources, and it is important to reference your sources when you do so. The examples in this part of Block 4 show you how to incorporate referenced material into a piece of writing.

In Section 2 there is a mixture of online and offline computer work. For the online work you will be using your computer to look at some e-government websites on the internet. In Section 4 you will use your computer to look at some animations which are designed to support the printed course material.

2 Scope of e-government

2.1 Modernising government

Before we start to look at e-government itself, I would like you to read some quotations. During the 1980s and 1990s, the potential of ICT systems for government was discussed by many commentators, but in the UK the official argument for e-government was set out in 1999 in the document *Modernising Government*. This document, however, is not specifically about e-government. Rather, it is about the much broader issue of how government should be modernised. Here is an extract:

> Earlier this year, a number of 'Integrated Service Teams' were set up to identify the practical problems facing people when they use public services. The teams looked at seven of the most common 'life episodes': leaving school; having a baby; becoming unemployed; changing address; retiring; needing long-term care at home; and bereavement. Some of the most common problems were:
>
> - People had to give the same information more than once to different – or even the same – organisations. A mother of a boy with physical disabilities said: 'I have lost count of the times I have had to recount my son's case history to professionals involved in his care.'
> - There is often no obvious person to help those most in need to find their way around the system.
> - There is a lack of integrated information to enable service providers to give a full picture of what help might be available.
> - There is minimal use of new technology. Most government Departments have a website, but few allow people to fill in forms on line. And government websites are not well linked to other relevant sites.
>
> Cabinet Office (1999), p. 23

Referencing: authors and page numbers

The referencing system used here is the author–date system, sometimes called the Harvard system. The author and date are given with the quotation, or near it. This is called the author–date citation, or just the **citation**. The citation is the link to the **reference** in the references list at the end. The reference supplies the full bibliographic information for the work cited. You can see my references list at the end of this part of Block 4. (Sometimes the references list is called a bibliography, though strictly speaking

citation

reference

a bibliography is not the same as a references list because it can include any relevant publication, whether cited or not.) Turn to the references list and find the reference for the quotation above.

It is not always clear who is the author of a source you are quoting from. This is often the case with official documents, so you have to decide as best you can whom to cite as author. When you are faced with this problem, it is sometimes helpful to look at online library catalogues, such as that of the Open University Library or the British Library, to see what name they give as the author. Enter the title of the document in the catalogue's search engine, and you should find details of the document. Another possibility is just to put the title in an internet search engine. This will sometimes produce a library catalogue record of the book.

Where does the page number go? If you only refer to the source once, the page number (or numbers) goes with the information in the references list. If there are multiple references to the same source, the best place is with the quotation, as here.

The use of capital letters, italics, quotation marks, brackets, etc. in references varies from publisher to publisher. However, it is usual to italicise book and journal titles.

Activity 1 (self-assessment)

Construct an author–date citation and a reference to accompany a quotation from page 35 of the following book: *The Rise of the Network Society*, by Manuel Castells, published in 2000 by Blackwell in Oxford. This is the sole reference to this book. You will probably find it helpful to look through the references at the end of this part of Block 4.

Comment

My answer is given at the end of this part. The answer also contains a note about edition numbers.

The extract from *Modernising Government* identifies typical problems ordinary people can have in dealing with government. The remedy for these and countless other problems, as far as this UK government document is concerned, is 'modernisation' of government, and part of this modernisation is the provision of services online. Typical online services would include: making tax payments, viewing a record of payments, contacting government departments and making appointments, finding information about entitlements, and so on. The first and last two bulleted points in the quotation are especially relevant. They point to deficiencies in information and services, and to a lack

of integration in what is available. This takes us to the heart of what many governments (not just the UK) view as the essential features of e-government:

- Making most, or even all, of the government's services available online.
- Bringing online services together, so that the user does not have to go to different departmental websites for different services.

In many countries, putting government services online did not begin with the launching of e-government projects. Individual departments had started to put their services online, both for their own use and for public use, well before these highly publicised e-government ventures were launched. However, a piecemeal approach has led to inconsistent systems, and one of the goals of e-government projects is to bring order and consistency to what would otherwise be chaotic.

Although making government services available online might be modernisation, would it necessarily be an improvement?

Activity 2 (exploratory)

Try to think of some clear advantages of electronic delivery of government services. You might like to look back to the bullet points in the extract above from Cabinet Office (1999) for some ideas.

Comment

These are my thoughts. Yours might be different.

Services would be available 'at a distance' – the user would not have to travel to them.

Services would be available round the clock.

Services might be cheaper, and might be better.

Official documents (white papers, bills, Acts of Parliament, etc.) could be more easily available as downloads from government websites.

Activity 3 (exploratory)

Can you think of any disadvantages that might follow from making these services available electronically?

Comment

Again, these are my thoughts. Yours might have been different.

People without access to online facilities might find that conventional services are less well supported than before, for instance by being poorly staffed or more awkward to use.

If government cost saving is a reason for introducing electronic services, this saving might be achieved by making the user do work that was formerly done by government staff (for instance, finding information, filling in forms, etc.)

The last two activities have raised the issue of cost saving, or potential cost saving. Some commentators have tried to gauge some of the cost savings from e-government. The following activity asks you to complete one writer's estimate of potential savings.

Activity 4 (self-assessment)

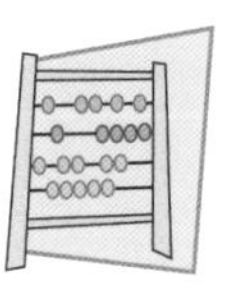

Rachel Silcock (2001) writes:

> [...] the Department of Social Security (DSS) handles around 160 million telephone calls each year (with mostly paper-based administrative systems), at an approximate cost of £2.40 per call (based on one of its most efficient call centres). If only 2% of these calls could be shifted to people looking up material on DSS web sites, then an annual saving of [...] might be achievable.

Fill in the missing figure in the last sentence of the Silcock quotation by doing the calculation. Hint: you will need to find 2 per cent of 160 million and proceed from there.

Comment

My answer is given at the end of this part.

Referencing: mentioning the author

If the author is mentioned in the sentence leading up to a quotation, as with the Silcock quotation in the last activity, putting the date in brackets after the author is usually the neatest way of giving the date. (If necessary, the page number can be included with the date.)

Note that by 'date' I mean just the year. If the publication were a monthly, weekly or daily (for instance) I would still give only the year. The precise date would be given in the references list.

Activity 4 showed that, in principle, substantial savings could be made if transactions with the government were done online.

The *Modernising Government* document initially set a deadline of 2008 for making 'all' UK government services available online. The 'all' was not meant literally. It excluded services which could not be delivered electronically or those for which 'there is genuinely unlikely to be

demand' (Cabinet Office, 1999, p. 62). A few years after *Modernising Government* was published, the 2008 deadline was brought forward to the end of 2005, and then relaxed somewhat to allow more exclusions. Nevertheless, the number of government services available online in the UK has expanded greatly, and the same is true of many other countries.

In 2005, Ian Watmore, the head of the UK e-Government Unit, was reported by Say (2005) as having said:

> [...] IT in government is as difficult as it gets. Government does things in IT which are more complicated than anywhere in the private sector.

Whatever the truth of this claim, it is not difficult to imagine that implementing e-government is particularly complex. Several issues occurred to me, and I have given them below. You can probably think of others.

- Technical issues. How are services to be made available online? Which services cannot be adapted to online delivery? For instance, can voting be done online in a way that everyone will trust? (At the time of writing, systems have been used in the USA that do not allow votes to be recounted, and lack many of the safeguards of paper-based balloting.) Can existing online services be made to work together? (We shall look at some of the issues with so-called legacy services later.)
- Cost. All large-scale ICT enterprises cost a lot. Will the benefits of introducing e-government justify the expenditure?
- Expertise. Large-scale ICT projects require a great deal of expertise to set them up, and a lot of expertise to keep them running. Is sufficient expertise available?
- Management. How do you manage a project such as this, both in the setting-up phase and the running phase?
- The **user interface** is what the user sees (and maybe hears) and interacts with. In an online environment where no one is available to help the user, how easy will it be to use government services?
- Usage. Will people want to use online e-government systems?

user interface

Issues raised by questions such as these are part of what makes e-government such a complex undertaking. In the UK, an idea of the scale of the e-government project can be gauged from the level and type of government support it has received. Rather than being supervised directly by a government minister, the project has been run by a specially appointed manager, a so-called e-Envoy, with considerable powers and access to high levels of government.

When thinking of services being made available electronically, it is natural to suppose that this means via computers. However, in the UK e-government project other methods of delivery are envisaged too:

> The strategy envisages that services will be accessed by multiple technologies, including web sites accessible from PCs, kiosks, mobile phones and digital TV, and call and contact centres.
>
> Cabinet Office (2000), p. 16

A couple of footnotes in the same document clarify what some of these terms mean:

> Kiosks are a means of providing access to electronic services in public places. Initially, kiosks tended to use touch-screen technology. More recently, keyboard input and web browsing have greatly improved their capability. [...]
>
> Contact centres combine the handling of e-mail, video and telephone calls.

There is no doubt, however, that access to government services via the Web has dominated thinking about e-government, and not just in the UK. This is what I shall concentrate on here.

2.2 Central and local government

In many countries, government can be thought of as having a central component and a local or regional component. In the UK, central government is based in London, although some functions are devolved to the Scottish Executive in Edinburgh, the National Assembly for Wales in Cardiff, and the Northern Ireland Assembly in Belfast (suspended at the time of writing). These devolved assemblies in Scotland, Wales and Northern Ireland are nevertheless forms of central government. Central government is generally concerned with such things as making laws, collecting national taxes (e.g. income tax, VAT), administering the armed services, national transport policy, determining policy on foreign relations, health, social security, and so on.

Local government is concerned with running local services, such as schools, health centres, public libraries, refuse collection, planning permission for buildings, etc. Funding for local services tends to come from a mixture of local taxes (for example, the council tax in the UK) and central government money. According to one UK newspaper, 80% of the public services that people are most concerned with are run by local government rather than central government (Cross, 2005).

Referencing without quoting

Referencing is needed sometimes even when you do not give a quotation. Drawing on data from another source generally needs a reference. In the Cross (2005) example above, no text is quoted, but there is a reference. This is because the statistic about 80% of public services is important, and possibly open to challenge. That is why there is a reference.

When the information you use is common knowledge, or can be found in dictionaries, encyclopedias and other reference works, you do not need to give a reference unless the information is contentious. Very particular information, such as statistical information, however, nearly always needs a reference.

In the UK, e-government is a matter for both central government and local government working collaboratively. However, Musgrave (2005) refers to:

> [...] gaps in understanding, and lack of collaboration, between officers in Local and Central Government Services. These findings are symptomatic of a cultural divide between Local and Central Government Services. The culture of non-cooperation across UK government is seen as the most substantial obstacle to sharing services, more so than legal or IT issues.

It is important to appreciate, therefore, that making e-government work successfully is not simply a technical matter. It depends as much on overcoming organisational and cultural differences between central and local government.

2.3 Styles of presentation

One commodity that is dispensed in vast amounts both by central and local government is information, and so this is one of the more obvious candidates for electronic delivery. Online government services are typically approached via a **portal** site, which is a kind of entry site from which other sites can be reached. The websites of large organisations, such as Microsoft, the BBC and the Open University, are usually portals.

portal

Going into a portal site is a bit like going into a large office building via the main door. Once inside, you have access to all the offices and departments inside the building, which are usually listed on a notice board. Similarly, portals list what is available, but in the form of a set of links. However, portal sites often have links to the sites of other organisations, as well as internal links to departments in the host institution.

An e-government portal site that only offered the user information would be a poor resource. The intention behind e-government is that sites should be transactional, that is, the user should be able to conduct a number of **transactions** at the site. Transactions involve such activities as paying, applying (for example, for a parking permit), consulting and booking. Transactions depend on the two-way flow of information between the user and the site. Transactional sites of any sophistication make extensive use of databases behind the scenes to hold data of many kinds. In fact, you can think of the site itself as an interface between the user and the many large databases that are needed to underpin the services offered.

transaction

In many e-government projects, online services are intended to become more personalised. Typically this involves either providing the user with a personal area on a portal, or providing something like a 'personal portal'. In a personalised online service, the site appears to 'know' relevant information about the user. For example, where he or she lives, the schools attended by members of the user's family, the status of tax payments, etc. This kind of service is intended to be convenient to the user. All the same, it can be disquieting to log onto a website and to find that the system apparently knows a great deal about you. You may have had similar feelings with book-selling websites that know all about your recent purchases and suggest more for you to make.

An example of a personalised site can be seen in the personal menu that Open University staff and students have (the students' version is www.open.ac.uk/studenthome).

Activity 5 (exploratory)

Go to your Open University personal menu and try to identify the ways in which it has been tailored to yourself.

Comment

The answers will vary, but the site was probably 'aware' of the course or courses you are studying. For instance, it shows your assessment scores on this course or any others you are studying. If you have already studied courses with the Open University it gives your course history.

A personalised portal, just like a transactional one, is underpinned by databases. Personalised portals should also allow the user to make transactions, which are similarly underpinned by databases. Thus, databases turn out to be a crucially important part of the substructure of an e-government system, as they are of many online systems. You will already be familiar with the essential idea of a database, but large-scale information systems such as e-government use more sophisticated databases. I shall discuss these in the next section.

Activity 6 (exploratory)

Find the official website of a local government authority in the UK. (If you live in the UK, you can use your own local authority or another.) A simple way to find a suitable website is to use the search terms 'council tax' (use double quotation marks) and the name of a town in a search engine. Not all the links produced will be to a local government website, but you should find one that is. Having found a suitable site, go to its home page and spend about five minutes exploring the facilities on offer. The purpose of this activity is just to familiarise yourself with some of the features of an e-government site.

Comment

Different local authorities have different sites, so I cannot give an overall comment. You probably found, though, that there was a certain amount of local authority information available, together with facilities for some transactions.

Towards the end of this part of Block 4 you will look at an e-government site in a more systematic way than you have done in this activity.

3 Databases

3.1 Tables and flat databases

Databases lie at the heart of many e-government systems, and at the heart of many other ICT systems. The local government websites you looked at in Activity 6, for instance, almost certainly used databases a great deal, as do the majority of central government sites. Away from e-government, the websites for Amazon or eBay, for example, use huge databases.

Constructing a database of any complexity requires careful thought about the way information is organised in any particular context. A database can therefore be regarded as the outcome of an analysis of the structure and use of information. The significance of this remark might not be clear at the moment, but should become clearer as you work through this section. Careful analysis of the structure and use of information is a vital part of all large-scale projects such as e-government.

relational databases

For large, complex information systems, **relational databases**, which I will describe shortly, are generally used, although relational databases can be used for simpler projects too. It is not the size of a project that dictates the need for relational databases, but its complexity. More specifically, the complexity of the relationships between information in the database is what dictates the need for relational databases. I hope to give you a flavour of what I mean by this in the short example in the following pages.

Relational databases are contrasted with simpler databases known as flat databases. Some people, however, use the term 'database' to mean only relational databases, and flat databases are sometimes simply called tables.

To understand what relational databases are and why we use them, we need to appreciate some of the shortcomings of the simpler, flat database. Table 1 is an example of a flat database. It contains information about some fictional students and the local authority evening classes they are studying. As you will recall, in a table like this a column can be described as a field, and each row is a record.

Table 1 Students and evening classes

Name	Address	Postcode	Course1	Course1_ Sessions	Course2	Course2_ Sessions	Course3	Course3_ Sessions
Lodhi, Mona	22 The Grove, Newport	AB12 3CD	Yoga	10	Holiday Spanish	15		
Jones, Bob	2 High Street, Stratford	AB6 4PQ	IT for all	5	Oil painting	15		
Cherry, Colin	59 Acacia Avenue, Brompton	AB2 12ZY	Digital photography	10	Sewing	15		
Cherry, Colin	13 The Limes, Leighton	XY6 7LR	Creative writing	20				
Edwards, Delia	40 Eldon Court, Hampton	XY12 4TK	Digital photography	10	Oil painting	15	Ballroom dancing	30
Roberts, Albert	18 Mount Pleasant, Greenhill	AB12 7UB	Drawing	15				
Singh, Sara	7 Marina View, Sutton	AB14 8WQ	Woodwork	15				
Chang, Patrick	21 Green Lane, Newport	AB12 9TU	Everyday maths	20				
Evans, Mary	13 The Limes, Leighton	AB6 7LR	Oil painting	15				

This table is quite short, but you could imagine it extending downwards to cover many more students.

Table 1 allows for up to three courses per student, and the fields for them are Course1, Course2 and Course3. Each course has an associated number of sessions, which is the number of classroom sessions in the course. This is shown in the fields Course1_Sessions, Course2_Sessions, Course3_Sessions. (I have avoided spaces in the field names because many database management systems do not permit them, but this is irrelevant to the principles I am outlining here.)

Table 1 could be set up as a spreadsheet. You can think of a spreadsheet as a flat database with a selection of built-in, simple database functions, such as searching and the ability to sort the data in various ways and to perform calculations on it (for example counting the number of students enrolled on each course). A spreadsheet also allows you to display the data as charts, graphs, lists and so on.

data type

Something that databases and spreadsheets share is the concept of a **data type**. Typical data types are 'text' (that is, alphabetic characters), 'number' and 'date'. Usually each field needs to be specified as holding a particular type of data. For example, in Table 1 the fields for course sessions would be defined as having the data type 'number'. Defining these fields as having numerical data allows arithmetical operations to be performed on the data, such as adding the number of course sessions in each record to find the total number of sessions a student has enrolled for. Similarly, using the data type 'date' allows data to be sorted chronologically. So, for instance, if there were a field with the starting dates of the courses, the records could easily be sorted into date order. A further benefit of defining a data type for fields is that it can help prevent the wrong type of data being entered. If a field is defined as containing text data (for instance), the program can perform checks on any data entered to make sure it is the right kind.

Table 1 is a very simple table. Much more data would need to be recorded in a real example, for instance course fees, classroom allocated, course leader's name, course code, start date, and so on. However, Table 1 has other problems which are not due simply to its lack of typical data. These other problems arise because the organisation of the data has not been considered carefully enough. I will come back to this point shortly.

Much of the usefulness of databases as a way of holding data arises from the fact that the data is organised, and can be interrogated in various ways. By 'interrogated' I mean that a question can be framed whose answer can be drawn from the database. For instance, a question might be: 'How many people with a postcode beginning "AB6" are enrolled on courses with 10 sessions or more?' For a human reader of Table 1, that question is easy to answer, although tedious if the table is big. Getting a computer to answer the question is not so straightforward, because the processes a computer would have to go through are quite complicated. In essence, a small computer program needs to be written to work through the data and to apply appropriate tests. This is done by using what is referred to as a **query language**. A query language is not quite like a natural language, such as English or French, but has some of the features of a natural language mixed with some mathematical features. A very common query language is **SQL**, or **structured query language**. You will see an example of a query using SQL later.

query language

structured query language (SQL)

SQL is often pronounced 'sequel', as well as being pronounced 'S-Q-L'.

3.2 Problems with flat databases

As a database, Table 1 is messy and inefficient, and does not really qualify as a properly constructed database. For instance, what happens if someone signs up to do four evening classes? To allow for this possibility we could incorporate further fields, such as Course4, Course5 and so on. But how many more fields should there be? If we choose an extravagant number, such as 20, we could be confident that no student would exceed that number of courses in a year, but the table would be wasteful as much of its content would be empty. (Even empty fields occupy space, because information about the structuring of the data must be stored whether the fields are empty or not.)

Another problem with Table 1 is the repetition of some items of data. For instance, the fact that 'Oil painting' has 15 sessions is recorded in three places in the table. A principle of good database design is to avoid repeated data such as this. When the same data is recorded in several places, there is always a possibility of clerical errors leading to inconsistency. What is more, changing the data or correcting errors means finding every repetition of that data in the table and changing it or correcting it. For instance, if the teacher on the Oil Painting course decided to add a few extra sessions, incorporating this amendment in Table 1 would mean updating several records. Ideally information about the number of sessions in a course would be recorded in just one place.

3.3 Entities and attributes

A well-designed relational database overcomes the problems outlined in Section 3.2 by using two or more tables, rather than a single table, such as Table 1. This means that the data has to be divided in some way between the tables. The construction of tables is done according to several rules. I will just look briefly at one rule to give you an idea of the underlying principles.

The rule I shall look at states that there must be one table per **entity**. An entity is an item for which we want to store information. It can be tangible – for example a person or an object – or intangible – for

entity

example an event. (Typical events might be a sale, registration or renewal.) An entity can be a concept – for example a bank account.

instance

attribute

In Table 1 the most obvious entity is 'student'. Any particular student, such as Colin Cherry, is an **instance** of this entity. Entities are the things we store data about in tables. Each piece of information we store is an **attribute** of that entity. An attribute is descriptive information about an entity. For the 'student' entity, attributes in Table 1 are name, address and postcode. In a properly constructed table there is one field per attribute.

You might argue that 'Course1', 'Course2' and 'Course3' are also attributes of 'student', and in some contexts that would be reasonable. In this case, though, there is descriptive information about courses, namely the number of sessions they run for. Courses therefore have attributes. In this context, then, 'course' is another entity. Whether something is regarded as an entity or not is dependent on the context.

Activity 7 (exploratory)

Does 'postcode' have any attributes in Table 1?

Comment

No. There are no attributes of 'postcode'. There is no descriptive information, or label or other qualifying information about postcodes.

I said above that in a properly constructed relational database we have one table per entity. Table 2 is the table for the student entity and Table 3 is the one for the course entity. I have added a few more fields to the tables to make them more realistic. For instance, Table 3 has a column for 'Fee' and a column for 'Course_code'.

Table 2 Student entity table

Student_ index	Family_name	Given_name	Address	Postcode
1	Lodhi	Mona	22 The Grove, Newport	AB12 3CD
2	Jones	Bob	2 High Street, Stratford	AB6 4PQ
3	Cherry	Colin	59 Acacia Avenue, Brompton	AB2 12ZY
4	Cherry	Colin	13 The Limes, Leighton	XY6 7LR
5	Edwards	Delia	40 Eldon Court, Hampton	XY12 4TK
6	Roberts	Albert	18 Mount Pleasant, Greenhill	AB12 7UB
7	Singh	Sara	7 Marina View, Sutton	AB14 8WQ
8	Chang	Patrick	21 Green Lane, Newport	AB12 9TU
9	Evans	Mary	13 The Limes, Leighton	AB6 7LR

Table 3 Course entity table

Course_ code	Course	Sessions	Fee
E01	Yoga	10	£20
E02	Digital photography	10	£20
E03	Everyday maths	20	£40
E04	Oil painting	15	£30
E05	Creative writing	20	£40
E06	Holiday Spanish	15	£30
E07	Woodwork	15	£30
E08	IT for all	5	£10
E09	Drawing	15	£30
E10	Sewing	15	£30
E11	Ballroom dancing	30	£60

The next step is to link the records in these two tables, which I will do shortly. Linking the records in separate tables requires the use of keys. A key uniquely identifies each record of a table. Table 1 did not have any keys. ('Name' cannot be a key because, as Colin Cherry shows, names might not be unique.) In Table 2 I have introduced a new column named 'Student_index'. Each entry in this new column uniquely identifies a particular record. The 'Student_index' in fact consists of just the sequential numbering of the records. This is the simplest way to create a key when there is no other key readily available.

The ultimate intention is to link students to courses through the keys. By associating a particular student with a particular course we have a way of representing an enrolment. We need therefore to think about a suitable key for Table 3.

Activity 8 (self-assessment)

In Table 3 I have not numbered the records as a key, as I did in Table 2, because I would like to use the course code as a key. How valid is the course code as a key under the following circumstances?

(a) Courses are presented only once, and never repeated.

(b) Courses are run only once per year, and repeated the following year.

(c) Some courses are run twice or more per year.

Comment

My answer is given at the end of this part.

In the following I am going to assume that the course code can be used as a key in Table 3; that is, the conditions in (a) or (b) of Activity 8 apply, with the proviso in the case of (b) that the database holds only a year's worth of data.

Splitting Table 1 into Tables 2 and 3 has lost the relationship between the entities 'student' and 'course'. We can no longer tell who is enrolled for what. The essence of the relational approach to database design is to relate entities to each other by relating their keys. In this example we would do this by constructing a **joining table** to capture the relationship between entities. Table 4 is my joining table. Student keys are on the left, and the keys from the courses table are on the right. To keep things simple, I am using the course code as the key although, as you saw in Activity 8, this is acceptable only under certain conditions.

joining table

I have annotated the table with names so that you can identify the records; but the annotations are not part of the table.

Table 4 Joining table for students and courses

Annotation	Student_index	Course_code
Mona Lodhi	1	E01
Mona Lodhi	1	E06
Bob Jones	2	E04
Bob Jones	2	E08
Colin Cherry	3	E02
Colin Cherry	3	E10
Colin Cherry	4	E05
Delia Edwards	5	E02
Delia Edwards	5	E04
Delia Edwards	5	E11
Albert Roberts	6	E09
Sara Singh	7	E07
Patrick Chang	8	E03
Mary Evans	9	E04

You will notice in Table 4 that student keys can appear more than once on the left, and courses can appear more than once on the right. This follows from the fact that the relationship between the student entity and the course entity is **many-to-many**. That is to say, one student can enrol for many courses, and each course can be taken by many students.

many-to-many

The entity tables and joining table taken together constitute the relational database. A real example might have many entity tables and many joining tables. It might also have no joining tables – for reasons I will come back to.

Notice how the new relational database solves the problems I identified with Table 1. If someone enrols for several courses, we just add more records to Table 4, as required. Each record in Table 4, therefore, represents the enrolment of a student on a course. We do not need to have empty fields available to accommodate additional enrolments by a student, as we did in Table 1. Also, if there is an administrative change to a course, such as the number of sessions, we need make only a single change, in Table 3. (You will recall that in Table 1, the repetition of the same piece of data in several places meant that administrative changes would require hunting out every occurrence of the data and modifying it.)

The process of organising data efficiently into tables, so that unnecessary repetition is avoided and so that each table represents a single entity and its attributes, is known as **normalisation**. The process we have gone through with Tables 1, 2, 3 and 4 is a very simple example of part of the normalisation process.

normalisation

In the light of the normalisation we have just done, we can criticise Table 1 in more appropriate language than before. The trouble with Table 1 is that:

- it contains data about more than one entity;
- it attempts to capture the relationship between entities.

It is therefore mixing different functions, and this is why it is unsatisfactory.

Activity 9 (self-assessment)

Table 5 is a flat database relating to some regular committee meetings. What are the entities and their associated attributes?

Table 5 Committee information

Committee	Meeting time	Member	Telephone number
Planning	Every Monday a.m.	Jones Patel Robinson	1239 4728 3589
Recreation	Every Friday p.m.	Jones Smith	1239 4633
Education	Final Wednesday of month, p.m.	Patel Robinson Smith	4728 3589 4633

Comment

My answer is given at the end of this part.

I mentioned that some relational databases might have no joining tables. The following activity is designed to show how this might come about.

Activity 10 (exploratory)

What would happen to the joining table, Table 4, if this particular local authority allowed people to enrol for only one course at a time? Write the first few rows of a new joining table on the assumption that each student takes only their 'Course1' as shown in Table 1.

Comment

Table 6 shows the first five rows of the new joining table. Notice that in Table 6 each student key appears only once, reflecting the fact that students are allowed only one enrolment at a time.

Table 6 Modified joining table: one course per student

Student_index	Course_code
1	E01
2	E08
3	E02
4	E05
5	E02

The relationship between the keys in Table 6 could be captured by a simple amendment to the student table, which would remove the need for a joining table. Table 7 shows the first few rows of the modified student table.

Table 7 Modified student entity table

Student_ index	Family_ name	Given_ name	Address	Postcode	Course_ key
1	Lodhi	Mona	22 The Grove, Newport	AB12 3CD	E01
2	Jones	Bob	2 High Street, Stratford	AB6 4PQ	E08
3	Cherry	Colin	59 Acacia Avenue, Brompton	AB2 12ZY	E02
4	Cherry	Colin	13 The Limes, Leighton	XY6 7LR	E05
5	Edwards	Delia	40 Eldon Court, Hampton	XY12 4TK	E02

You can see that Table 7 now has a new field, for the course key. This new field links records in Table 7 to those in Table 3, and lets us see enrolments at a glance. No joining table is needed.

The additional key in Table 7 (the course code) is known as a **foreign key**. Using a foreign key has enabled us to dispense with the joining table, but only because the relationship between students and courses is no longer many-to-many. When the relationship between entities is many-to-many, a joining table is needed.

foreign key

Activity 11 (self-assessment)

Suppose Table 5 is to be normalised into separate tables for the 'Committee' entity and the 'Member' entity.

(a) Why is a joining table needed?

(b) Construct the joining table, using Committee as one key and Member as the other.

Comment

My answer is given at the end of this part.

This is as far as we shall go in constructing relational databases. The important point to appreciate from this brief introduction to the topic is that even a fairly simple example has called for a careful analysis of the nature of the information and how it is related. Many large-scale information systems succeed or fail on the quality of the analysis, and the quality of the design that follows from the analysis.

Some of the processes of database construction can be done automatically. For instance, if you construct a table like Table 1 in Microsoft Access, the program itself can make a reasonable attempt at creating entity tables and joining tables for you. However, for large-scale information systems, such as those involved in e-government, there is no substitute for a careful study of the nature of the information, its relationships, and its uses.

3.4 Using a query language

When you search a large website for information, for instance when you search a large e-government site, very often, behind the scenes, a large relational database is being searched. I mentioned earlier the use of SQL as a way of extracting information from a database. Depending on the system being used, your enquiry may be converted into an SQL query, and this finds the information you need. For example, suppose we wanted to find the family names of all people enrolled on the digital photography

course (E02) in the last section. Below is an SQL query to find this information. (There are other ways to construct this query using SQL.)

SELECT FAMILY_NAME

FROM TABLE_2 JOIN TABLE_4 ON
TABLE_2.STUDENT_KEY = TABLE_4.STUDENT_KEY

WHERE COURSE_CODE = 'E02'

You are not expected to be able to create or interpret SQL queries. This is provided as an illustration.

I will briefly explain how the query works. It is based on the idea of merging Tables 2 and 4 ('Table_2 join Table_4'), subject to certain constraints. One constraint is that the student_keys must be equal ('On Table_2.Student key = Table_4.Student_key'). In effect, the merged table is like Table 2, but with an extra column giving the course codes for each student. However, the only records included in this table are those for which the course code is E02, as specified in the condition 'Where course_code = 'E02''. The first instruction ('select family_name') retrieves the required information from this joint table.

3.5 Other kinds of data

All the data we have had so far in the database has been text or numbers. I have mentioned that another type of data might be dates. Modern databases, however, can store other kinds of data than text, numbers and dates. They can also store graphics, moving pictures and sounds.

Activity 12 (exploratory)

What complications might there be when incorporating pictures, sound clips and moving pictures in a database?

Comment

The following three points occur to me:

Files for pictures, sound clips, etc. are often very big. This is not an insuperable problem, but often, rather than incorporate the file in the database, a link to it is incorporated. This is a pointer to where the file might be found.

Users of the database need to be able to view the data. This is not usually a problem if the data is text, numbers or dates, but needs special provision if it is not. Imaging and audio software might need to be incorporated, therefore, in the database software so that users can see graphics or hear sound.

Users of databases need to be able to search for data. With graphics, sound or video files it is usual to store associated descriptive text (or keywords) along with the file so that a search can find it.

A common example of a database that incorporates non-text and non-numerical data is the photograph-album software that comes with many digital cameras. This enables the user to archive their digital photographs, along with textual data, such as title, date, camera settings and so on. On a bigger scale, databases relating to large groups of individuals, such as library users, employees, criminals and so on, increasingly include such non-text items as photographs, vocal recordings, fingerprints and iris scans. These are examples of biometric data, which we shall look at in the next section. Biometric data is used to help identification – photographs being perhaps the most obvious example.

Activity 13 (self-assessment)

(a) What are the two main types of database?

(b) What is an entity?

(c) What is the purpose of a joining table?

Comment

My answer is given at the end of this part.

3.6 Viewing the data

Reverting to the relational database we constructed in Section 3.3, you might wonder what, from the user's point of view, has been gained by creating separate tables for the students and courses. With Table 1 you could see at a glance who was studying what. In the relational database it was hard to see the same information. However, with databases (relational and flat) the user does not normally view tables directly. Generally data is viewed in a 'form', which is a specially designed interface between the user and the database. Figure 1 is an example.

Course code E01
Course title: Yoga
Sessions 10
Fee 20
Start date 01/10/2006
Course centre The Cedars,
Course centre postcode MK11 2XY
Students
Lodhi, Mona
22 The Grove, Newport
AB12 3CD 0191 32355
A N Other
A N Other

Figure 1 Form view of a database

The rectangular boxes in Figure 1 show the field values of a particular record or set of records. The user can scroll or jump forwards and backwards though the records, or search on any field for a particular piece of data.

Not all the fields of a database need be shown in the form; and some of the displayed data might be extracted from the database through the use of a query language, such as SQL, though generally the user is insulated from the complexities of the query language. The fields in Figure 1 are labelled for ease of identification, for example 'Course centre postcode', 'Start date', and so on. These labels are design features of the form; they need not be the same as the entity names or attribute names. The arrangement of the fields in the form can easily be redesigned for ease of use without affecting the underlying data in the tables. In fact, there are few limits to the way data can be viewed in a form view.

Another way to view data is for it to be 'rendered' for viewing on a web browser. This is a bit like a form view, except that the form is created by HTML code. For example, when you look at your Open University personal web page, you are viewing data that is taken from large relational databases, but rendered for viewing on a web browser. The same goes for some of the interactive facilities you would have seen on some of the government websites.

3.7 Databases and XML

In Table 1, it was easy to see which pieces of data belonged to which fields, where the records began and ended, and so on. The tabular layout enabled us to see at a glance the salient features. If you wanted to find a particular name in a table, you ran your eye down the 'name' field. It is a different matter for a computer. How does a computer 'know' which pieces of data belong to which field? How does it look in the right places? The data on the hard drive or in the RAM is not even arranged in a tabular way.

structure

For a human user, a tabular layout gives a **structure** to the data. When data is structured, it is clear where a piece of data begins and ends, and which record and field a piece of data belongs to. For the computer to be able to work in a similar way with data, the data needs to be structured in a way that the computer (or rather, the program) can interpret. Different database systems have different ways of recording where data begins and ends, and which fields the data belongs to. Often additional data is incorporated into the database for this kind of 'housekeeping', but it is hidden from the user. This extra data is used by the program to encode the structure of the data. Word-processor files similarly contain data that is hidden from the user – for instance, instructions to display certain pieces of text bold and other pieces as italic.

Different database programs demarcate the structure of data in different ways, and this has proved to be a major problem in the e-government projects of many countries. Consider, for instance, accessing a government portal in order to use a particular service. You might have to log on, supplying a username and password. Behind the scenes, verification processes will check these and either allow you to proceed or not. You might then move on to other parts of the system to investigate, for example, your entitlement to benefits or to check tax liability.

Although you may have entered the e-government website via a single portal, behind the scenes the data required for these activities will typically be held in several different proprietary database systems. This is because of the long history of piecemeal implementation of databases in central and local government. Typically there will be no common standard for coding the data fields in these databases. For example, in one system addresses might have fields with names such as House number, Streetname, Town, City, Postcode and so on. Another system might have Address1, Address2, Address3 instead. This is an example of the 'legacy problem'. In many cases it is too expensive to replace these diverse systems with new, integrated systems operating to common standards. Somehow the older systems have to be incorporated into the newer e-government systems and have to be able to work together with them. A vital tool for enabling these diverse systems to work together has been **XML**, or eXtensible Markup Language, which I will briefly discuss.

XML

The idea of marking up goes back to pre-computer printing technology. The (human) printer would be supplied with a typescript of the document to be printed. The document would be 'marked up' with handwritten tags or labels (Figure 2).

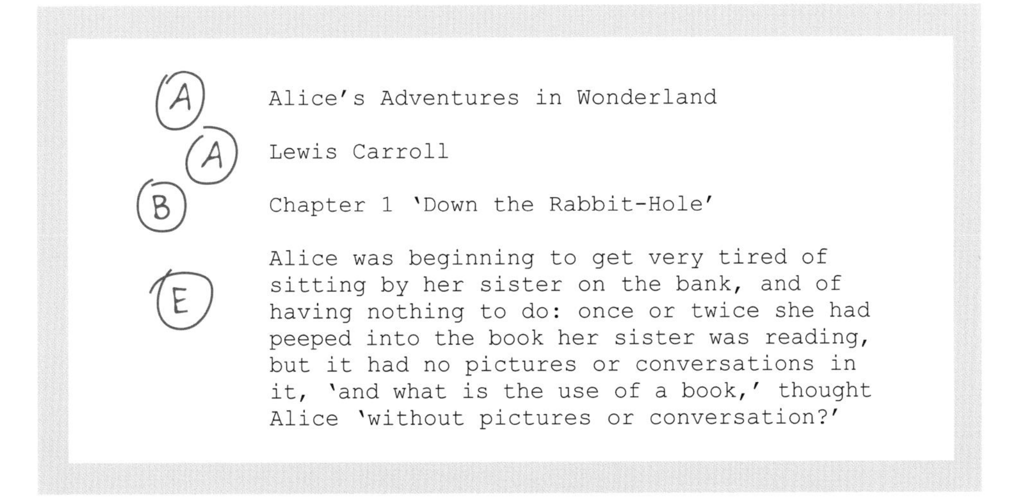

(A) Alice's Adventures in Wonderland

(A) Lewis Carroll

(B) Chapter 1 'Down the Rabbit-Hole'

(E) Alice was beginning to get very tired of sitting by her sister on the bank, and of having nothing to do: once or twice she had peeped into the book her sister was reading, but it had no pictures or conversations in it, 'and what is the use of a book,' thought Alice 'without pictures or conversation?'

Figure 2 Use of tags for marking up

The tags were coded instructions for particular fonts and sizes, and an accompanying sheet explained what they represented. The meaning of the tags would change from typescript to typescript; the tags did not have fixed meanings that applied to all typescripts the printer would work on.

schema

Tagging is a way of keeping appearance and content separate. In Figure 2, the typescript is the content, and the appearance (how the text should look on the page) is embodied in the tagging. XML uses this idea of tagging to indicate the form or structure. As with the print markup, XML tags have no fixed meaning, and so any particular XML document needs an accompanying definition of what the tags represent. This is usually done in a **schema**. Although to some extent XML resembles HTML, the need for a schema in connection with XML documents is a crucial difference. In HTML there is no schema, and the meanings of tags are set down in a standard.

One difference between XML coding and the old style of print mark-up is the embedding of XML tags within the content of the document itself, rather than their being in a reserved part of the document. (In the case of the print mark-up, the reserved area is the margins.)

Activity 14 (exploratory)

What safeguard is needed if tags are embedded in the text itself?

Comment

The most important safeguard is that the tag should not be interpreted as part of the content of the document. This is usually done by surrounding the tags with special characters (or symbols). XML uses angle brackets, < and >, as HTML does. Notice that in the print mark-up, the tags are encircled as a further aid to keeping them separate from the content.

As an example of XML in practice, Figure 3 shows a small StarOffice spreadsheet. (StarOffice uses XML coding in all its files.)

	A	B	C
1	Animal	Number	Date
2	Cat	21	01/05/53
3	Dog	75	25/07/64
4	Horse	36	03/11/84
5	Parrot	29	30/11/04
6			

Figure 3 StarOffice spreadsheet

Below is a *small* part of the XML file for this table. Don't worry about trying to understand it. I have picked out some of the data items from Figure 3 in bold. Notice how little of this extract is content, and this extract is just a small part of the entire file.

<table:table-row table:style-name="ro1">
<table:table-cell><text:p>**Animal**</text:p></table:table-cell>
<table:table-cell><text:p>**Number**</text:p></table:table-cell>
<table:table-cell table:style-name="Default"><text:p>**Date**</text:p></
table:table-cell></table:table-row><table:table-row table:style-
name="ro1">
<table:table-cell><text:p>**Cat**</text:p></table:table-cell>
<table:table-cell table:value-type="float"
table:value="21"><text:p>**21**</text:p></table:table-cell><table:table-
cell table:value-type="date" table:date-value="1953-05-
01"><text:p>**01/05/53**</text:p></table:table-cell></table:table-
row><table:table-row table:style-name="ro1">
<table:table-cell><text:p>**Dog**</text:p></table:table-cell>
<table:table-cell table:value-type="float"
table:value="75"><text:p>**75**</text:p></table:table-cell><table:table-
cell table:value-type="date" table:date-value="1964-07-
25"><text:p>**25/07/64**</text:p></table:table-cell>

From what you have learned about HTML you will recognise the use of symbols like < > and / to distinguish parts of the file that deal with layout from parts that deal with content. HTML and XML have both evolved from an earlier mark-up language called SGML (Standard Generalized Markup Language), devised for use with print documents.

Many proprietary ICT systems use coding to keep information about appearance and content separate. Two things make XML different from proprietary equivalents:

- It is an open standard. Its openness means that it is not owned by any particular company.
- It is extremely adaptable to new ways of distributing and presenting information.

These two factors make XML invaluable as a common language for exchanging structured data. However, by itself XML does not solve the legacy problem. In addition, there need to be various types of **middleware** to translate legacy data into XML, and to translate in the opposite direction. (Middleware is a general name for software that can enable separate systems to work together.) Middleware is specific to particular systems, so solving the legacy problem also involves the appropriate middleware. This might mean buying it, but in some cases it means creating it specially.

middleware

XML is widely used where different systems need to operate together, and not just legacy systems. For instance, through the adoption of standard schemas for data exchange, banks can swap information easily among themselves, even though their information systems are very different. Many other types of business use XML to allow for standardised ways of transmitting information. XML has also been influential in the growth of **web services**. Web services are self-contained reusable programs that are components of online services. Examples are authentication of identity, currency conversion, shipping processing, etc. The programs that perform web services are self-contained units, and can be incorporated directly into a more complex online service.

web services

platforms

These services need to be able to work on many different **platforms**, that is, in many different computing environments, with many different programming languages. The open nature of the XML standard has allowed this to happen. XML is also increasingly used 'behind the scenes' in word-processing documents, spreadsheets, databases and online documents and forms.

The impact of XML on information exchange and online provision of services has been enormous and will almost certainly continue to grow. Bisson (2005) wrote:

> Tomorrow's XML will also be much more visible in the foreground of computing. Computer desktops will become canvases for active documents that mix XML data and formatting information – and include links to web services. Your online tax return will be a document that looks like the paper forms the Inland Revenue sends, but it will be able to work with online calculation services, before delivering XML data directly into the Inland Revenue systems (and automatically transferring your refund into your bank account).

The development of XML has been very timely for the e-government project because it has allowed incompatible systems to work together. However, XML is only part of a much bigger picture. In the UK, the government has set up an e-GIF (e-government interoperability framework) initiative, which is a set of compulsory standards for the public sector of the UK. These standards define the way that data should be structured and accessed. For instance, the e-Gif framework specifies the use of web browsers for viewing data, the use of XML for integrating data, the use of internet and Web protocols, and so on. Systems that are 'e-Gif compliant' (i.e. which conform to the e-Gif specifications) should be able to communicate between themselves. A European e-Gif system is under development at the time of writing.

The increasing ease of transfer of data is practical and convenient. But is it always in the best interest of the people whose data is held? People who have investigated the data held about them by, for instance, credit

card companies, have often been surprised at the amount of data held, and questioned whether much of it was relevant to the business of credit card companies. In the context of e-government a particular concern is the ease of transfer of data from one government department to another, so that, for instance, a person's medical records or tax record might be viewable by other departments. Another concern is that personal information could be made available to private companies. With the contracting to private companies of work formerly done by government departments, private companies often need access to the information held in government databases.

3.8 Data modelling and databases

The subject of databases becomes very complex with deeper study. This is not so much because database software requires great skill to make it do what is needed, but because database design begins with a deep understanding and analysis of what the entities and attributes are, and the relationships between entities. This is **data modelling**, and very little of it has anything to do with computers; rather it is much more about studying carefully how organisations work, how information is acquired and used, who uses it and how, and so on.

data modelling

Databases probably impinge on our lives more than we realise. As we have seen, they underlie many websites of any complexity, but they also underlie great swathes of the e-government project, as well as billing systems from utility companies, booking systems for holidays, personal records held by employers, banks, credit card companies, and so on. The list of applications of databases goes on and on. In addition, databases are essential components of modern telecommunications, for instance in the routing of data packets on the internet. They are also essential to electronic systems of personal identification, which is what I will look at next.

4 Biometrics, identification and verification

4.1 Data and biometric data

Developing alongside the various e-government projects around the world are many biometric systems for authenticating identity. Governments have traditionally had a stake in the authentication of a citizen's identity through issuing passports, driving licences and other so-called identity documents. However, this is yet another area where ICTs are having a transforming effect, perhaps not to everyone's liking:

> At America's insistence, passports are about to get their biggest overhaul since they were introduced. They are to be fitted with computer chips that have been loaded with digital photographs of the bearer (so that the process of comparing the face on the passport with the face on the person can be automated), digitised fingerprints and even scans of the bearer's irises, which are as unique to people as their fingerprints.
>
> A sensible precaution in a dangerous world, perhaps. But there is cause for concern. For one thing, the data on these chips will be readable remotely, without the bearer knowing. And – again at America's insistence – those data will not be encrypted, so anybody with a suitable reader, be they official, commercial, criminal or terrorist, will be able to check a passport holder's details. To make matters worse, biometric technology – as systems capable of recognising fingerprints, irises and faces are known – is still less than reliable, and so when it is supposed to work, at airports for example, it may not.
>
> *The Economist* (2005)

In this section we shall look at some of the techniques and issues related to the authentication of identity using biometric data.

biometric data

Biometric data is derived from distinctive bodily features. Examples are fingerprints, photographs, iris patterns, and so on. 'Biometric data' also covers data derived from characteristic behaviours or gestures, for example signatures or vocal characteristics. Converting this data to digital form allows it to be processed automatically by computers. This is a distinct change from older methods of identification which depended on a good deal of human inspection (for instance, visual inspection of fingerprints). Biometric data is increasingly incorporated into passports, driving licences and other identity documents.

Whatever method of identification is used, comparison of one piece of data with other data is involved. For instance, in criminal investigations,

fingerprints collected from the scene of a crime are checked against records of fingerprints from known criminals.

For an identification system based on data comparison to work, there must be authoritative samples of data, from known individuals, to compare with. The bank of fingerprints held by the police is a collection of such data. But two specimens of data from the same person are hardly ever identical – for instance, the signature I write on a cheque is not identical to the one on my cheque card. Whether my cheque card confirms the signature on my cheque is a matter of judgement.

In the following pages, I would like you to keep in mind these two essential components of identification systems:

- Authentic data, known to be associated uniquely with a particular individual, is required for comparison.
- Reliable methods are required for comparing pieces of data and for deciding whether they are from the same person.

We shall look more closely at the implications of these requirements shortly, but first I should say a little more about what I mean by 'data' in the context of identification systems.

4.2 Data for identification

I have already mentioned signatures, photographs and fingerprints as examples of the kinds of data that have been used for authenticating a person's identity. Many other types of data have been used or suggested. DNA is widely used, but mostly in criminal investigations. Iris recognition, which relies on distinctive patterns in the coloured part of the eye, is another technique. Figure 4 shows a collage of iris patterns.

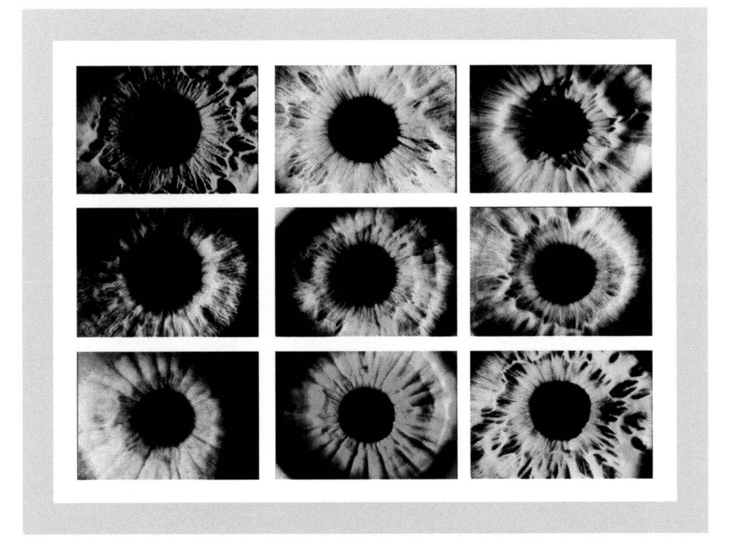

Figure 4 Iris patterns (courtesy of Dr John Daugman, Cambridge University)

Whatever type of personal data is used, it needs to be unique for each individual. The fingerprinting system depends on everyone having different fingerprints. Facial recognition depends on no two faces being the same. Iris patterns appear to be unique to each individual. In fact, the patterns in the left and right eyes of the same individual are different, and identical twins have different iris patterns.

Activity 15 (exploratory)

What advantages for identification does biometric data have over non-biometric data such as names and addresses, passwords, etc.?

Comment

Two advantages occur to me. The first is that everyone's biometric data is (or is believed to be) unique, whereas non-biometric data sometimes cannot be guaranteed to be unique. The second is that biometric data should be harder to steal than non-biometric data.

For many decades the only biometric data that was routinely used to authenticate someone's identity was photographic data. For instance, passports and membership cards have traditionally had photographs. However, the development of ICT has opened up possibilities for using other kinds of data. With biometric data in a digital form, comparison of data becomes a mathematical operation that can be computerised, rather than requiring human checking. I can illustrate this with a highly simplified example.

Suppose a piece of biometric data consists of a person's numerical scores on three different criteria (maybe eye separation, eye size and eye colour). One person's data might consist of the binary equivalent of the three numbers 24, 7 and 125, where each number represents the value of a different physical property. Another person's data might be 26, 6 and 122. Each number in the second set of data is close to the corresponding number in the first set. A computer could calculate how close this second set of data was to the first by comparing each of the three numbers in turn. A preset threshold can be applied such that if the two sets of data are closer than the threshold they are judged to be a match. If they are not closer than the threshold, they are not a match. Note that although the comparison can be computerised, the threshold itself is set by a human.

Biometric data is not immune from theft or forgery. There are cases of people making a cast of someone else's finger and using it to gain access to systems that use fingerprint recognition (Bowcott, 2004). A disadvantage of biometric data is the difficulty of restoring security once it has been breached. For instance, if a user's fingerprint has been copied, a replacement fingerprint cannot be offered, whereas a replacement password can easily be issued.

4.3 Identification systems

At the time of writing, biometric identification is not in widespread use, although that situation is likely to change. There are, however, a few schemes which have been used, and I would like to look at two of these now. The first is the experimental EyeTicket JetStream iris-recognition system that was used for passport-free immigration control at Heathrow airport in the UK in 2002. The scheme, which ran for about six months, was used only on travellers who had enrolled in it. To enrol, applicants had iris scans taken of their eyes. Figure 5 shows enrolment in a similar system at Schiphol airport.

Figure 5 Enrolment in the iris-recognition system at Schiphol airport, Amsterdam. The woman at the back is having her iris scanned. The woman at the front enters the data into a database (courtesy of Dr John Daugman, Cambridge University)

In the Heathrow scheme, and many others, the biometric data acquired during enrolment was stored as a **template** in a database of enrolled users. The template in this case was not a digital photograph of the eye, but a digital representation of data from the iris scan. An analogy would be a file that recorded eye colour, separation of eyes, diameter of iris, and so on. However, in the case of iris scans the data relates to the patterns of markings shown in Figure 4. The template can be quite small in data terms. In one system, the iris data in the template has a size of 256 bytes. In other systems, however, templates are digital photographs of the eyes.

template

Enrolment in the Heathrow scheme involved not just taking a scan from the applicant and entering it into the database, but also checking whether this person's scan matched any of the templates already in the database.

Activity 16 (Exploratory)

Why might the applicant's scan have matched a template already in the database? More than one answer is possible.

Comment

There are two possibilities to account for the person's biometric data matching an already existing template.

1. The applicant's scan was similar enough to someone else's template to be within the threshold. This is always possible, although ideally it will be rare. (You will see why mismatching is possible shortly.)
2. The applicant was trying to enrol a second time, and matched their already existing template.

In the first comment on Activity 16, the applicant is innocent of any subterfuge. In the second case, the applicant might or might not be innocent. For instance, the applicant might have forgotten their earlier enrolment, or might be enrolling under a different name having legitimately changed their name (for example through a change of marital status). On the other hand, the applicant might be dishonestly trying to enrol a second time under a different name. This last possibility is a particular concern with the issuing of identity cards, which in the UK will also serve as entitlement cards for benefits and other services.

In the Heathrow experimental scheme, if the enrolment happened without complications, then on subsequent visits to Heathrow the traveller would look into a scanner at immigration control. This would take an iris scan, which would be compared with all the templates in the database. If there was a match with one of the templates, then the person was regarded as having been identified, and passed through without needing to show a passport.

Similar systems to the Heathrow one are used at several airports to ensure that only authorised staff can get to restricted parts of the airport. In Japan they are also used for access control in some residential apartment blocks. At the entrance, the resident looks into a scanner, and if their scan matches a template in a database they are allowed in. A common feature of all identification systems is this process of taking a sample of data when authentication is needed and comparing it with an entire database of templates.

A rather different type of identification system is used in the United Arab Emirates. All inward travellers to the country at all entry points have iris scans taken with machines like that shown in Figure 6.

Figure 6 Iris-recognition system in the United Arab Emirates. In the photograph, the scanner is obscured by the man's head

These scans are checked against templates for a 'watchlist' held on a central database. The watchlist consists of about 400 000 individuals who, for various reasons, are to be denied entry. If no match is found, then the traveller is allowed through and completes the normal immigration procedures.

Activity 17 (exploratory)

In the Heathrow and United Arab Emirates systems, a match between the traveller's data and a template in the database had different outcomes. How did the outcomes differ?

Comment

In the Heathrow experimental system, a match with a template meant the traveller could proceed, whereas in the United Emirates System a match meant the traveller could not proceed.

The difference mentioned in the last activity indicates that identification systems can be used in two different ways. In the Heathrow system, the assumption was that most checks result in a match, whereas in the United Arab Emirates system the presumption is that most checks do not result in a match. This difference is sometimes expressed in terms of **positive identification** and **negative identification**. Positive identification is a check on whether someone is a member of a particular set of people. Negative identification is a check on whether someone is not a member of a set of people.

positive identification

negative identification

What characterises an identification system is that it checks whether a particular individual is known to the system. This is the check that was made in both the Heathrow experimental system and the United Arab Emirates system. An identification system does not necessarily identify the person. However, it is not difficult in principle to extend identification systems so that they do establish a person's identity. Suppose you have templates for every citizen of a country in a database, together with personal data about the people the templates were taken from. This system could theoretically act as a national identification scheme. At any point where identification was required, the person could supply a sample of biometric data (perhaps by looking into a scanner), and this would be checked against the entire national database. If there was a match, then the person's name and address could be shown. Through links to other databases, other personal information could theoretically also be brought up, such as medical records, police records, employment and social security records, and so on. Such a scheme, if it could be made to work, takes us into ethical and political issues, which I will return to later. For the moment, there are questions of feasibility to consider, arising from the problem of so-called false matches.

4.4 False matches and false non-matches

I mentioned earlier that one of the essential components of an identification system was a reliable procedure for comparing data. Ideally, one person's biometric data would never be mistaken for another's, and one person's biometric data would always match another sample from the same person. Unfortunately such perfection cannot be achieved in practice. Errors happen because samples of biometric data taken from someone on different occasions are almost certain to be different, just as two specimens of my signature are different. This means that establishing someone's identity by looking for an exact match between biometric samples is not possible.

The practical solution is to look for a certain level of similarity rather than exact sameness. To count as a match, two samples of biometric data need to be sufficiently similar rather than identical. What are the implications of this fact? We can get an insight into their implications by thinking about Figure 7. The two faces represent samples of biometric data, and the arrow represents a comparison. Clearly the samples are different, but are they from the same person?

Let us suppose that these samples are from the same person. To be fairly sure of getting a 'Yes' verdict in the comparison, we should set the threshold of similarity at a fairly low level. That is, our comparison system should be quite tolerant of differences between samples of biometric data. That increases the likelihood of the right verdict: 'Yes. These are from the same person.'

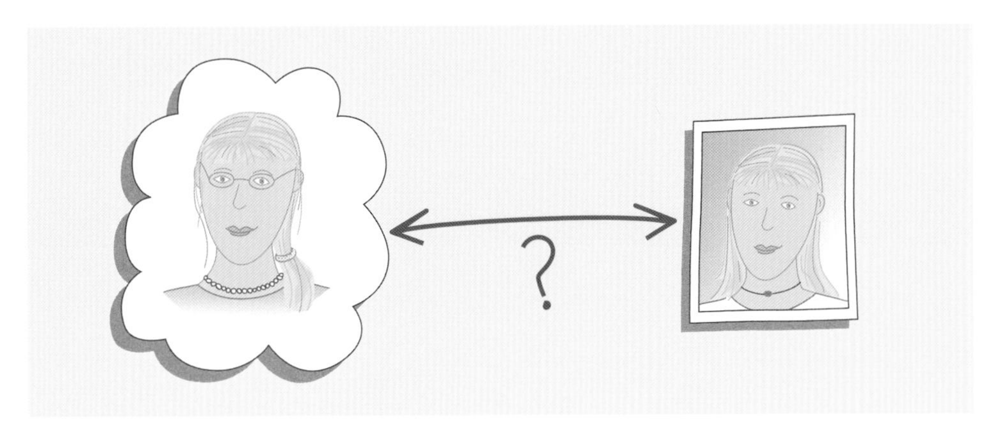

Figure 7 Comparison of biometric data

But suppose the two samples of data in Figure 7 are from *different* people. If the comparison is tolerant of differences, these samples will be judged to be from the same person, which is the wrong answer (in this case). To increase the likelihood of the correct verdict when the samples are from different people, the comparison needs to be *less* tolerant of differences.

As you can see, there are conflicting requirements here. To ensure that samples of data from the same person match we need a fairly relaxed criterion of similarity. But to ensure that difference is detected, we need a strict criterion.

These two types of error are known as false match and false non-match. They are illustrated in Figure 8.

A **false match** is when two pieces of biometric data from different people are judged to be from the same person, as in Figure 8(a). This type of error is sometimes called a **false accept**. It results from a comparison that is too tolerant of differences.

false match

false accept

A **false non-match** is when two pieces of biometric data from the same person are judged to be from different people, as in Figure 8(b). This type of error is sometimes called a **false reject**. It results from a comparison that is too intolerant of differences.

false non-match

false reject

Activity 18 (self-assessment)

(a) Which type of error is increased by relaxing the matching criterion, and why?

(b) Which type of error is increased by making the matching criterion stricter, and why?

Comment

My answer is given at the end of this part.

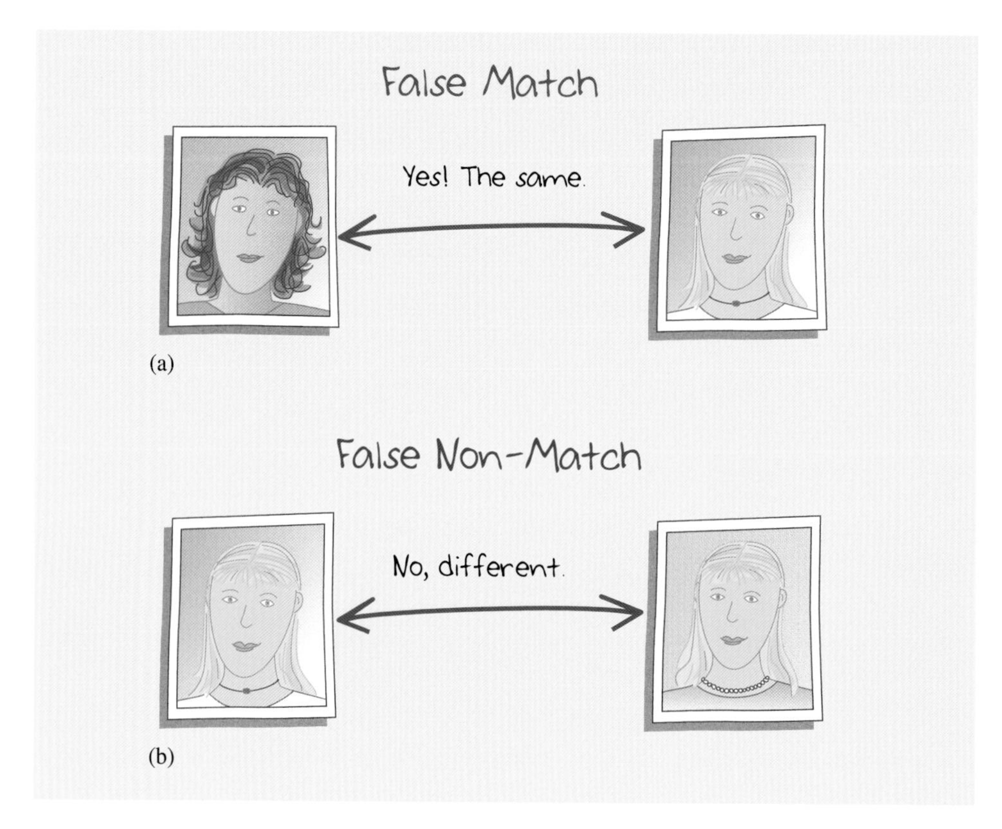

Figure 8 Two types of matching error

False matches and false non-matches are not caused by the use of ICT-based systems or by the use of biometric data. They can happen when any type of data is assessed for similarity by any type of inspector – human or otherwise.

The performance of biometric systems is gauged by various statistics. One of these statistics is the false match rate. The following section looks at some typical false match rates.

4.5 Typical false match rates

A false match rate is expressed as a statistic such as '1 in 1000'. A rate of 1 in 1000 means that if a sample of biometric data is compared with random selections of other data, a false match occurs, on average, once every 1000 comparisons. False match rates vary widely between different biometric systems. The following figures are taken from Mansfield and Rejman-Greene (2003).

Using good-quality fingerprints, a false match rate for single prints can be around 1 in 100 000. This rate can be improved by using more than one finger. Low-quality prints give worse rates.

Face recognition gives a false match rate of around 1 in 1000.

For single-eye iris recognition, Mansfield and Rejman-Greene (2003) quote a false-match rate of 1 in 1 000 000. Using two eyes improves the rate considerably.

These rates do not allow you to predict how many false matches there will be in any single small-scale test. For instance, a system with a false match rate of 1 in 1000 when tried on a group of 10 or 100 people might or might not produce false matches. The outcome is unpredictable. However, with a large group the result becomes more predictable. For instance, a system with a false match rate of 1 in 1000 when tried on a group of 1 000 000 people will produce about 1000 false matches. This figure comes from dividing the group size, 1 000 000, by 1000, which comes from the false match rate of 1 in 1000. However, this method is only an approximate one, and can be used only with large groups. What we mean by 'large group' or 'small group' depends on the false match statistic. For instance, if the false match rate is 1 in 100, a group size of 10 000 is quite large; but with a false match rate of 1 in 100 000, the same group size of 10 000 is small.

Activity 19 (self-assessment)

The false match rate of a particular biometric system is 1 in 100. A sample of data is compared against 1 000 000 other randomly chosen pieces of data. Approximately how many false matches can we expect?

Comment

My answer is given at the end of this part.

The lesson to draw from the last activity is that if the number of comparisons is sufficiently large, then a lot of false matches can result, even if the false match rate appears to be quite low. This needs to be borne in mind when thinking about identification systems for a whole population.

Deciding which biometric system to use is not just a matter of picking the one with the best false match statistics. The figures given above are laboratory figures, and whether the same performance can be obtained in practice, when conditions are not ideal and the participants may be impatient or uncooperative, is another question. Also, there is the question of how a system would work in practice. Would it require people to stop and do something, potentially causing bottlenecks at busy places such as airports, or could it operate on people while they were doing something else, without their being aware that an identity check was being carried out, as with face recognition? Considerations like these play a part in deciding which system to use.

4.6 False identification

If you think back to the Heathrow experimental system and the United Arab Emirates system described earlier, you can see that the false matches and false non-matches open up possibilities for these systems to malfunction. In the Heathrow scheme, a false match could mean that a person who was not enrolled might be allowed through. In the United Arab Emirates scheme, a false non-match might mean that a person who should be stopped is allowed through. These are examples of identification error. The following activity looks at these two types of error.

Activity 20 (exploratory)

Work your way through the computer animation called *Identification and verification*, which is on the T175 DVD. It will take about 15 minutes. The animation reviews the material you have already studied on identification, and introduces the concept of verification, which you will study shortly.

Comment

The animation shows that the rate of false positive identification depends on two things: the false match rate and the size of the database. For example, if a system has a false match rate of 1 in 1000, when used on a database of 1000 (or bigger) it is virtually certain that there will be a false positive identification with someone in the database. Thus, the false positive identification rate in this case approaches 100% (1 in 1), because of the large size of the database. A false positive identification rate of 100% means that every time a sample is checked against an *entire* database, there is at least one false match somewhere in the comparisons.

Besides reviewing the idea of identification, the animation has introduced the concept of verification, which we shall come to shortly.

false positive identification

To summarise what you saw in the last activity, **false positive identification** arises from a false match with a template belonging to someone enrolled in a database, as shown in Figure 9.

The rate at which this happens depends on both the false match rate and the size of the database.

Note that it is possible for a piece of biometric data to falsely match more than one template in the database. It is also possible for a piece of biometric data to *correctly* match one template, and to falsely match one or more other templates.

Figure 9 False positive identification error. The subject's data is tested against the entire database and falsely matches one of the templates

We have probably all experienced false positive identification error when we see someone we think we know, say 'Hello' to them, and then realise it is not the person we thought it was. Something about them looked familiar, but the similarity was deceptive.

false negative identification error

False negative identification error arises from failure to match the person with their own template in a database (Figure 10).

When there is false negative identification, it is conceivable that the person's data could falsely match someone else's template. However, this is irrelevant to the meaning of false negative identification, which is strictly about the failure of a person's data to match their own template.

We have probably all experienced false negative identification when we fail to recognise someone we already know, possibly because they have changed their appearance or because we meet them in an unfamiliar context.

4.7 Identification errors and the national database

The UK identity card scheme, and similar schemes in many other countries, is based on the idea of creating a national identification register. This is a database that will have templates of biometric data from all citizens. In the UK, the proposal is to have a photograph, some

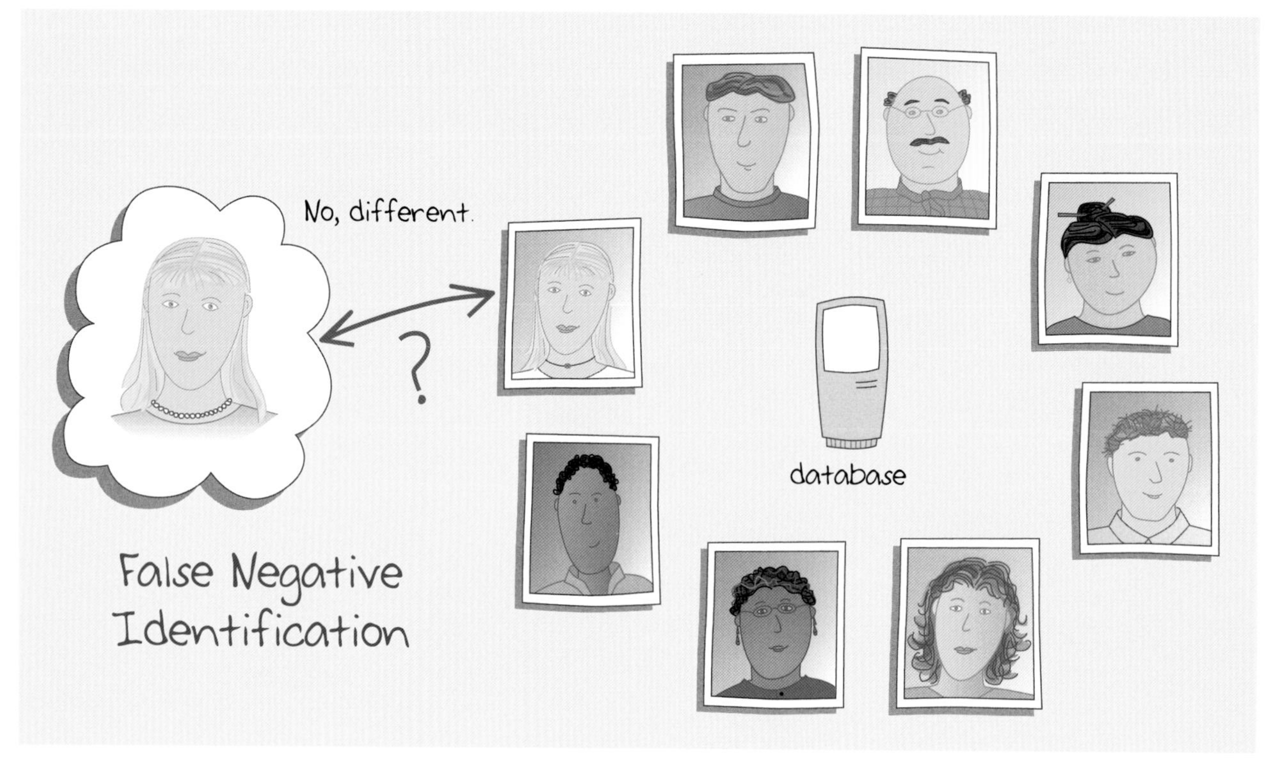

Figure 10 False negative identification error. The subject's data is tested against the entire database and fails to match the same person's template

fingerprint data and iris scans from each citizen. There will also be other data in the register: name, address, national registration number, and much more besides. Identity cards will be issued only to people who are enrolled in the national identification register. This latter point is crucially important to the system envisaged for the UK.

Much of the controversy about identity cards relates more to this national database of personal data than to the cards themselves. In the next few activities, you will be looking at extracts from an article by Roger Dettmer that looks at the practicalities of creating a national identification register. As you will see, Dettmer is essentially concerned with identification errors, and his observations apply equally to any national-scale identification system.

Activity 21 (self-assessment)

Read the following extract from Dettmer (2004). Note that in this and subsequent extracts you might not be able to understand all the details, but you will probably be able to follow the argument.

(a) Briefly explain why Dettmer sees false negative identification as a security problem, whereas false positive identification is not. Remember that false negative identification is failure to recognise

someone already enrolled. False positive identification is misidentifying one person as another.

(b) Why does usability require a low probability of false positive identification?

Comment

My answer is given at the end of this part.

Safety in Numbers

R. Dettmer

November, 2004

IEE Review

Consider the problem of issuing ID cards [identity cards]. A primary concern of the authorities will be to prevent the issuing of an ID card under two or more, unconnected, identities (allowing, for example, a card holder to make multiple, fraudulent claims for benefit). When an individual, Mr Brown say, applies for an ID card, his biometric will be collected. If this is a first application, then the biometric should not match the biometric of anyone already enrolled in the identity register, and Mr Brown's details and biometric can be added as a new entry. If Mr Brown is already registered, then the biometric search should reveal details of the previous application, preventing him from establishing a second fraudulent identity.

In this instance, the relevant biometric errors are:

- False negative identification error – the biometric search fails to find the previously enrolled biometric, presenting the risk of a fraudulent application
- False positive identification error – the individual's biometric erroneously matches that of another person already enrolled, requiring further checks against the possibility of a fraudulent application.

Usability [ease of use] requires a low probability of false positive identification, while security requires a low probability of false negative identification.

Reading technical articles

The Dettmer extract for the last activity was quite short, and perhaps did not cause you undue trouble. The extract in the next activity is longer and might not be so straightforward.

It is easy to get demoralised if you are reading a technical article and find it hard going. If that is how you feel, you are in good company. Very few people find technical articles easy to read, and few experts would expect to be able to understand everything in

an article. In fact understanding an article is not an 'all or nothing' business. There are degrees of understanding, and for many experienced readers understanding is approached by stages. Very often the first read through is quick, to get a general impression. On the basis of that, there's a decision to be made: Do I persevere, or have I got everything from the article I want to get from it at the moment? If the decision is to persevere, then the next reading is more methodical. One of the jobs on subsequent readings is to isolate the parts that are hardest to understand. You might even need to go to other articles on the same subject to see if they have another approach that makes more sense to you. Alternatively, you might need to spend time thinking about what you have read and rephrasing it in your own words.

I am not expecting you to go looking for other articles on this subject, nor to spend a long time thinking about it. The important point to remember is that it is normal not to understand everything in an article like this. However, here are a few tips to help you.

- Generally each paragraph is making one main point, or maybe just a few related points. Try noting these down.
- The overall argument is usually carried by the main points, rather than the details, so try to see the story that the main points are telling.
- The last one or two paragraphs often contain the major points the author wants to make. It is all right to read those first, and to use that information to fill in some of the parts you are struggling with.
- Often if you reread an article after a gap of a day or two, parts that were difficult to understand turn out not to be so difficult after all.

one-to-one

one-to-many

For the next extract, you need to know the meanings of a couple of the terms Dettmer uses. A **one-to-one** comparison is when you compare one piece of data with another. In this context, those pieces of data are biometric data. A **one-to-many** comparison is when you compare one piece of data with many others. In this context that might be when you compare a piece of biometric data with all the templates in a database.

Activity 22 (self-assessment)

Now read the second extract from Dettmer (2004), and answer the following question: Why does Dettmer say that a biometric identity system will need to be based on taking iris scans from both eyes, or fingerprints from eight fingers?

Comment

My answer is given at the end of this part.

Since each identification involves a comparison against the entire set of prior enrolments, error rates for this one-to-many identification search will depend on the size of the database. Can biometrics deliver acceptable levels of usability and security when we're matching individuals against a database of around 50 million? With several thousand applications per day, if the rate of false positive identification is much more than 1 in 1000, the workload of further identity checks would be unmanageable. Thus 1 in 1000 is the target rate for the one-to-many false positive identification error rate. When the identification is made against the entire database, it would involve some 50 million one-to-one comparisons. As a National Physical Laboratory feasibility study on the use of biometrics indicates (http://www.homeoffice.gov.uk/docs2/feasibility_study 031111_v2.pdf), to obtain this level of performance the false match error probability for one-to-one comparisons (the probability that a comparison between Mr Brown's biometric and an individual database entry results in a false match), ought to be smaller than 1 in 10^{10}.

According to the NPL study, a good fingerprint system might achieve a false match error rate of 1 in 10^5 using a single finger; the false match rate for a single iris is better than 1 in 10^6, while for facial recognition the false match rate is more typically 1 in 10^3. Thus the NPL study recommends that, in order to uniquely identify one person in a population of 50 million, a fingerprint system should use at least four fingers per person, preferably eight; an iris system should use both eyes, and facial recognition could not, on its own, provide a sufficient accuracy of identification.

Facial biometrics could be used as an aid to identity checking for passport holders. In this instance, which is a one-to-one comparison, the relevant usability parameter is the one-to-one false rejection rate [false non-match rate]. SmartGate, a pilot study of a face recognition passport control system at Sydney International Airport, revealed a false rejection rate of approximately 1 in 50. This is reasonably encouraging. However, the SmartGate study was restricted to less than 4000 Qantas aircrew and it is by no means certain that the same results would be obtained when applied to a larger, possibly less co-operative, user base.

Dettmer describes a one-to-one comparison here in which biometric data is collected and compared with a single template on a passport or other identity document. The data is not compared with all the templates in a database.

Irrespective of the likely error rates for SmartGate-type systems in 'real world' applications, the ICAA's [International Civil Aviation Authority] choice of facial biometric remains controversial – 'a grave error' in the opinion of Professor John Daugman, the inventor of the dominant iris-recognition algorithm.

Before we look at a final extract from Dettmer, I want to make a short detour into verification. This is because documents such as identity cards, passports, driving licences and the like are, strictly speaking, for verification of identity rather than for identification. Increasingly these documents have biometric data in memory chips incorporated in the document.

4.8 Verification

You will, perhaps, by now be getting a sense of the challenge of setting up an identification system on a national scale. However, for many routine purposes, establishing who a person is from an entire population of possibilities is not what is required. Instead what is required is confirmation that the person is who they claim to be. This is **verification**. An example of verification happens when you collect a parcel from a depot. You are sometimes asked to show your driving licence, passport or other suitable document. This document verifies your identity.

verification

Verification, like identification, involves a comparison of data, at least when done properly. If I sign for the parcel when I collect it, my signature should be checked against the one in the verification document. Alternatively, if the verification document has a photograph of me, the person issuing the parcel should check me against the photograph.

What distinguishes verification from identification is the number of checks made. In identification, data I supply (or which is taken from me) is checked against an entire database of templates. With verification, my data is checked only against data in the verification document. To use the terms you have already met, identification involves one-to-many checking, whereas verification involves one-to-one checking.

Because verification involves just a single comparison, it offers some advantages over identification. One advantage is that a biometric template can be stored in the verification document itself, in a machine-readable chip. The Schiphol airport system shown in Figure 5 uses this method. Travellers who enrol in the system receive a membership card containing a memory chip. The chip holds the member's biometric template. When passing through the airport, the traveller puts the card into a reader and stands in front of an iris scanner. If the scan matches the template on the card, the traveller passes through immigration control without further formalities.

Another advantage of verification over identification relates to false positive identification. In identification, biometric data has to be checked against every template in the database. The large size of a national database can make false identification quite likely. However, in verification there is only a single check – against the template in the verification document. In fact, in verification we are much more likely to be concerned with false non-matches than with false matches. For example, an enrolled traveller at Schiphol airport would be highly inconvenienced if his or her iris scan did not match the template on the chip. This is a false non-match.

Naturally verification is only as reliable as the document used for verification. As the extracts from Dettmer's article have shown, enrolling

users in the proposed UK national identity card scheme requires that the applicant be checked against an entire database of previous applicants before the card can be issued. In other words, enrolment depends on an identification system. Only when an applicant has been successfully checked against the entire database is the verification document issued. This feature distinguishes the UK identity card system from those of some other countries.

In the next activity you will be working with the final part of Dettmer's article.

Activity 23 (self-assessment)

Now read the final extract from Dettmer (2004), and answer the following question.

Dettmer foresees problems in setting up a national identity card scheme. Does he see these problems as relating to identification or to verification? Illustrate your answer with one or two short quotations. (There is no need to supply references for your quotations.)

Comment

My answer is given at the end of this part.

> Assuming that the underlying technology could be made to work – possibly by using different biometrics in combination to obtain the requisite levels of performance – there remain huge question marks over the basic practicality of the whole idea of a biometrically based national ID card. In particular, we need to know how long it will take to enrol users in a real system; what percentage of the population will be unable to provide the required biometric (apparently around 1 in 70,000 of the population is born without an iris); what percentage of the population will be unable to travel to their local 'biometric registration centre'; how such exceptions can best be handled; and, assuming the scheme is self-financing, how much people will be prepared to pay for an ID card. The list just goes on and on.
>
> [...]
>
> In the interim, and substantially beyond, there is clearly still much to do. No country in the world has, as yet, attempted to create a biometric scheme on the functionality and scale envisaged by the UK's ID card scheme and you don't have to be remotely paranoid to find the whole prospect more than a little scary.

Dettmer's anxieties, as revealed in the article, relate to the practicalities of the system. Will there be so many identification errors as to make it unworkable and undermine the public's trust? Can people be enrolled fast enough? And so on. However, for many other critics, anxiety is based much more on the principles than on the practicalities. I shall look at some of these concerns now.

4.9 Ethical, social and political aspects

The introduction of identity cards has proved controversial in several countries, for example France (where identity papers have long been a requirement) and Australia. Generally the issues have related to the questions like: 'What are these cards actually for?', 'Whose interests do they serve?' and 'What use will be made of the underlying database of identity data?' Opponents of identity schemes have pointed out that totalitarian regimes have always found identity systems very useful – Nazi Germany and South Africa under apartheid being frequently cited. Even if a present-day government is trustworthy, what assurance is there that a future government will not abuse an identification system? Debates in this field are thus as much ethical, political and social issues as they are technical.

Ethical, political and social issues

Ethical, political and social issues differ in many ways from purely scientific or technical ones. With purely scientific and technical disagreements, there is usually a route to a solution that is agreed on by the disagreeing parties. Thus, although all parties may be convinced of their rightness, they can usually agree on what would be required to settle the dispute. For instance, they might agree that performing a particular experiment or building a prototype device would settle the argument. Behind this 'agreed route' idea is the notion that accumulating more facts, or evidence or data will settle the dispute. (In the event, this new data might not settle the disagreement, but the parties will nevertheless agree that this is the way disagreements are settled.)

Ethical, political and social disputes, in contrast, have a different character. With them there is usually no agreed route to a resolution. Although the parties in the dispute may cite data and facts to support their positions, there is not likely to be any crucial evidence that will settle the dispute. In fact, the basis of the dispute often relates to the significance of factual evidence, for instance, whether a particular fact is more or less significant than another. In other words, the debate is about the value that should be attached to factual data.

In technology, issues often arise that inextricably mix science, ethics, politics and social questions. Biometric identification is a good example, but there are many more. As you have seen, there are concerns about gathering personal information about citizens and about the uses such information might be put to. These are ethical issues. Underlying them are questions of rightness or wrongness in a moral sense, rather than in a scientific or technical sense.

You have also seen that there are concerns about whether the state should be able to do certain things, such as compelling citizens to participate in an identification scheme. Questions such as these, which relate to the holding and exercising of power, are examples of political issues.

Finally, as you have seen, there are concerns about the type of society that might result from national (and international) identity schemes. Will some sections of society be disadvantaged relative to others, and will individual liberty be infringed unacceptably? These are examples of social questions, as they relate to the organisation and running of society.

Distinguishing between the technical aspects and the ethical, political and social aspects of an issue is often not easy. To help to clarify the distinction, it can be useful to think how a dispute could be resolved. If there is a route based on factual data, then it is probably a technical matter. If there is no clear route involving factual data, then there are probably ethical, political and social aspects. For instance, deciding how many fingers need to be used to achieve a particular performance level in a fingerprint identification system looks like a technical matter; but deciding whether national fingerprint data should be made available to the police does not. Even purely technical matters, though, often need to be seen within a larger ethical, political or social context. For instance, a technical question about identification might have very different implications within a totalitarian regime compared with a tolerant regime.

In this section I am going to look briefly at some of the issues in a UK context, although they are not confined to the UK. I am drawing heavily on an article by Dempsey (2005) for this section although I am not quoting him.

Dempsey (2005) points out that in the UK, government arguments for an identification scheme have shifted. At one time identity cards were promoted as part of the campaign against terrorism. This argument has tended to be played down in favour of arguments about reducing benefits fraud. It is claimed that the careful checking of identity that precedes the issuing of a card will make it harder for fraudsters to make multiple claims with different identities. Commentators have questioned both of these arguments. Unless suspected terrorists are on a watch list, it is hard to see how identity cards can thwart them. Furthermore, many authorities have pointed out that benefit fraud usually results from dishonest declaration of income by the fraudster. The fraudster's identity is usually not false, so the usefulness of an identity card looks questionable in this case too. Other critics have pointed out that forged

identity cards will almost certainly be available to anyone with the time and money to acquire them, so an identity card system could lead to a false sense of security.

There is certainly a case to be made for the practical usefulness of identity cards. For many low-level verification tasks, UK citizens currently have to use passports and driving licences in the absence of anything more suitable. This suggests a need for some sort of identity document. Many critics worry, however, that cards will come to be required for all sorts of activities that have not needed them traditionally, such as booking a hotel or buying travel tickets. This might seem no more than a nuisance, but many people who are not criminals nevertheless have good reasons to want their true identity kept secret (for instance, if they have fled from abusive domestic circumstances). Life for them would be more difficult. Criminals, on the other hand, who will always be able to get forged cards, will hardly be inconvenienced.

Although the controversy over identification schemes is usually expressed in terms of identity cards, what is at issue is often not so much the cards themselves as the national database, or national identity register, that would underpin the scheme. For many objectors, the creation of a large database containing everyone's photographs, fingerprints and other personal data looks like an erosion of traditional liberties. Hitherto, the only people who have had their fingerprints routinely collected have been criminals. Does collecting biometric data from everyone turn them, potentially, into suspects?

The creation of a national identity register could be argued to be consistent with 'modernisation of government' – the justification for so much of the e-government project. Almost any large business nowadays gathers information on its customers and stores it in a database. Compiling information on customers is part of the modern way of doing business. Why should it be different for a government? Managing a country could certainly be much simpler and more efficient if accurate, up-to-date information on the population was available all the time from a national database, rather than only intermittently via periodic censuses.

The convenience and usefulness provided by a national database, however, would not be confined to government. Many private organisations would find access to that kind of information attractive, and might be willing to pay for it. Critics of the identity card scheme suspect that information from the national identification register would find its way into private hands.

Other anxieties centre on the blurred distinction between identification and surveillance. It would, for instance, be possible for a facial-recognition system to be used in conjunction with surveillance cameras, so that a particular individual's movements could be automatically tracked in an area surveyed by cameras. Dempsey (2005) records that

traffic cameras from the UK were used for surveillance of student demonstrations in Tiananmen Square in Beijing, China, in 1989.

Looking to the future, it looks likely that identification systems in different countries will require some degree of standardisation. Within Europe, for instance, some countries' identity cards contain only a photograph of the owner and name and address. In some cases the cards are not backed up by a national database of biometric data.

My final point relates to cost. A national-scale identification system will be expensive. A UK identity card scheme, for instance, would be one of the largest IT projects ever undertaken. If the justification for the system is, say, crime reduction, could a better result be obtained by spending the money in other ways? Many critics of an identity system argue that it could, although the UK scheme is intended to be largely self-financed from the cost of enrolment.

This section has given only a brief coverage of some of the ethical, political and social issues involved with an identity system. However, there is plenty of further material on the Web.

Activity 24 (self-assessment)

Which of the following questions clearly raise ethical, political or social issues, and why?

(a) Which biometric system has the best false match rate?

(b) What information should be held on an identity card?

(c) How much should citizens be charged for their identity cards in order to cover the cost of setting it up?

(d) Which type of data chip on an identity document is most easily read remotely?

(e) During enrolment, how should cases of false positive identification best be handled?

(f) On what occasions should citizens be required to identify themselves, and who should have the right to demand identification?

Comment

My answers are given at the end of this part.

5 Usability and accessibility

5.1 Introduction

usability

The word **usability** has cropped up a few times already in this part of the block. In the context of biometric identification, usability referred to the smoothness of enrolment and other tasks associated with setting up an identification system. A system that produced few false matches during enrolment of applicants was described as usable.

Another meaning of usability is related to the ease of use of an interface. Although this meaning of the term is often used in the context of computer interfaces, there is no reason to confine it to computers. The concept of usability applies equally well to the design of tools and implements, or to noticeboards, for example Figure 11.

Figure 11 Noticeboard in a park

Activity 25 (exploratory)

How would you rate the usability of the noticeboard in Figure 11? If you think it would not be easy to use, what is the cause of the problem or problems?

Comment

When I came across this sign, I was puzzled for a while, so I did not rate its usability very highly.

All the distances are on the right of the board and aligned. It makes for a consistent style of presentation, so that distances can always be found on the same part of the board (there were other noticeboards like this one in the park). From that point of view the board conforms to generally accepted principles of 'good design'. However, as a user, my first impression was that the right-hand side of the board related to things to the right of the sign, and the left-hand side of the board

related to things to the left of the sign. The arrows seemed to support this view (especially the puzzling second line of the board, which has arrows in both directions).

In the context of e-government, usability is of particular concern because the public is unlikely to adopt the new systems of delivery of services if they are difficult to use.

5.2 Usability principles

Usability as a field of study has grown rapidly with the spread of computers, the Web, mobile phones and other portable ICT devices. Although there are some basic principles of good, usable design, there are no rules that guarantee a good design. In this respect design for usability is like other branches of design, such as industrial design, book design or interior design.

Usability design draws on ideas from psychology, ergonomics, typography and so on, and makes extensive use of feedback from users. Feedback is gathered using various techniques, such as questionnaires, observation of users, interviews and recordings of users in action. Recordings of users can take many forms also, for example timing, video recording, recording users' spoken commentaries, and tracking software that records all the key strokes made by a user.

Like virtually all areas of design, usability design is (or should be) **iterative**. That is, a prototype is tried, evaluated, modified in the light of evaluation, tried again, and so on. It is especially important to try a prototype with the kind of people who will use the finished product. Sara Bly, who designs and evaluates interfaces, says:

iterative

> Recently I was asked to design and evaluate an application for setting up personal preferences and purchasing services on the web. I was told it would be hard to test the interface 'in the field' because it was difficult to get a 45–60 minute test period when the user wasn't being interrupted. When I pointed out that interruptions were normal in the environment in which the product would be used and therefore should occur in the evaluation too, the client looked aghast. There was a moment of silence as he realised, for the first time, that this hadn't been taken into account in the design and that the interface timed out [that is, closed down after a period of inactivity, with loss of data already entered] after 60 seconds. It was unusable because the user would have to start all over again after each timeout.
>
> Bly (1997)

human-centred design (HCD)

This focus on the users of the system is an example of the **human-centred design (HCD)** approach. The HCD approach is intended to ensure that aims of the interface or service are fulfilled for real users. The term 'users' is understood to mean not just the customers or members of the public who use the interface for a particular service (sometimes referred to as **end users**), but also the people who have to operate and maintain the system.

end users

The principles of good design for e-government systems are not significantly different from those for other systems. For instance, Cabinet Office (2003), *Quality Framework for UK Government Website Design*, offers these pieces of advice (among others):

> A good government website should have some content that has been specifically written for the Web [...][and] should not simply repeat printed brochures [...]
>
> Writing for the Web is a specific skill.
>
> Cabinet Office (2003), p. 30.

Jakob Nielsen, who has written extensively about usability, similarly says that writing for the Web is very different from writing for the page:

'Scannable text' is text the reader can easily skim.

> People rarely read Web pages word by word; instead, they scan the page, picking out individual words and sentences. [...] As a result, Web pages have to employ scannable text [...]
>
> Nielsen (1997)

Activity 26 (self-assessment)

The following two pieces of text are directed at managers of an e-government project, and offer advice on dealing with web designers. Which would be better suited for online presentation, and why?

(a) 'A web designer should make it clear from the start what they will need you to do to quickly and effectively build your website. Content will be the major requirement. Indeed, it is often this aspect of putting together a website that takes the greatest amount of time, as the content must be collated and optimised for the Web. Ensure you have your content completed to the deadline you have agreed. This will ensure the designer/agency has no excuse concerning the completion of the project on time.' (Cabinet Office, 2003, p. 44)

(b) A web designer should make it clear what you need to do. Content will be your major contribution to the site.

Assembling content often takes longer than anything else. This is because it needs to be:

- collated
- optimised for the Web.

Be sure to observe your deadlines, so that the designer/agency cannot blame you if the project runs late.

Comment

My answer is given at the end of this part.

Nielsen's reason for advocating scannable text is not just because it is easier to read, but because it helps the viewer decide whether the text is worth reading. This is important because Web use is as much about deciding whether a page looks useful as it is about reading what is on the page. As further aids to scannability, Nielsen advises the use of:

> highlighted keywords (hypertext links serve as one form of highlighting; typeface variations and colour are others)
>
> meaningful sub-headings (not 'clever' ones)
>
> bulleted lists
>
> one idea per paragraph (users will skip over any additional ideas if they are not caught by the first few words in the paragraph)
>
> the inverted pyramid style, starting with the conclusion
>
> half the word count (or less) than conventional writing
>
> Nielsen (1997)

In the 'inverted pyramid style', the first sentence gives the gist of the following text. What follows fills in the details. This style is used in popular journalism.

The price paid for concise web pages is loss of context and detail, but these can sometimes be supplied in other ways, for instance by headings, clear links and highlighted keywords, all of which Nielsen advocates.

The authors of *Quality Framework for UK Government Website Design* point to the importance of a search engine:

> [A]n effective site-specific search engine is crucial to most good government websites.
>
> Cabinet Office (2003), p. 33

Once again, this advice agrees with Nielsen's view of good practice:

Navigation here means the set of hyperlinks joining pieces of text or pages.

> Search is the user's lifeline when navigation fails. Even though advanced search can sometimes help, simple search usually works best, and search should be presented as a simple box, since that's what users are looking for.
>
> Nielsen (1998)

In fact, for many users a search facility is not a second choice, to use when navigation fails, but a first choice that is often quicker and simpler than the navigation facilities.

Nielsen has at various times summarised his thoughts on usability in a list of principles. Here is one such list, slightly simplified by Preece et al. (2002).

1. Visibility of system status. Always keep users informed about what is going on, through providing appropriate feedback within reasonable time.
2. Match between system and the real world. Speak the users' language, using words, phrases and concepts familiar to the user, rather than system-oriented terms.
3. User control and freedom. Provide ways of allowing users to easily escape from places they unexpectedly find themselves, by using clearly marked 'emergency exits'.
4. Consistency and standards. Avoid making users wonder whether different words, situations, or actions mean the same thing.
5. Help users recognise, diagnose, and recover from errors. Use plain language to describe the nature of the problem and suggest a way of solving it.
6. Error prevention. Where possible prevent errors occurring in the first place.
7. Recognition rather than recall. Make objects, actions, and options visible.
8. Flexibility and efficiency of use. Provide accelerators [for example, keyboard shortcuts] that are invisible to novice users, but allow more experienced users to carry out tasks more quickly.
9. Aesthetic and minimalist design. Avoid using information that is irrelevant or rarely needed.
10. Help and documentation. Provide information that can be easily searched and provides help in a set of concrete steps that can easily be followed.

Nielsen's principles apply to all types of computer interface, for example the interfaces to operating systems, word processors, calculators and so on, not just web interfaces.

Principles like these give you an evaluative framework, but they are not in themselves a quick tool for evaluating an interface. For instance, an interface that falls short on two of these principles is not automatically better than one that falls short on three. The evaluation has to take into account the way the interface is used, which will probably (among other things) lead to some principles counting for more than others.

Activity 27 (exploratory)

In this activity you will take part in an informal survey of the facilities and usability of UK local government sites. You need to choose a suitable site. Ideally it should be a site you are not familiar with, so you should probably choose a different site from the one you used in Activity 6. Read through the following directions before beginning.

(a) Check whether the site allows you to do the following, or has the following features. Record your results in the Usability Survey on the T175 website (at the end of the Block 4, Part 3 main page). Also, note how much time it takes you to do this part of this activity.

   (i) adjust appearance – font size
   (ii) adjust appearance – colour
   (iii) use a screen reader
   (iv) make payments online
   (v) access information in other languages
   (vi) find library opening times
   (vii) search the site.

(b) Note how long it takes you to do (a). Record your result in the survey.

(c) Assess the ease of use of the site. Record your result in the survey (very poor, poor, OK, good, excellent).

(d) Note the URL of the site you have assessed. Record it in the survey.

Comment

A real usability survey would, of course, have several people investigating a single site, rather than have them investigating a range of sites. In that respect this activity is unrealistic. It should be viewed therefore as a kind of progress report on the usability of e-government sites in general.

5.3 Accessibility

accessibility

In Section 5.1 you assessed the usability of Figure 11, the noticeboard in a public park. For a visually impaired person, that noticeboard might not be usable at all, as you may have commented. This raises the issue of **accessibility**. Accessibility relates to how well a service is adapted to the diverse abilities of all potential users. Disabled people and people with various kinds of impairment have an interest in accessibility, but accessibility is not exclusively concerned with their needs. For example, users of online services might be using mobile phones or PDAs (personal digital assistants) to access the services, or might have slow connection speeds. If people have difficulties using the services because of their equipment, then they have accessibility problems. Accessibility therefore overlaps to some degree with usability.

Activity 28 (Exploratory)

How might a web designer cater for users with slow connections?

Comment

One of the most useful ways of catering for users with slow connections is minimising the total size of files that are downloaded when web pages are accessed. Large files take a long time to download and therefore cause delay. The solution is usually to avoid large graphics files, sound files or video files. Sometimes a text-only version should be offered.

Generally designers want their sites to be usable and accessible by all users, in so far as that is feasible. In the UK, at the time of writing, there is also a legal dimension: disabled people have a strong legal case if they can show that failure to take account of their needs has disadvantaged them.

adaptive technology

assistive technology

Some of the features required for good accessibility are easy to envisage. For instance, some users need to be able to adjust font sizes, screen resolution, and so on. Other users might find particular combinations of foreground and background colour make text hard to read. However, the accessibility implications of other features of interfaces are not so readily apparent. Some users, for instance, have a screen reader, which uses a synthesised voice to read on-screen text aloud. Other users have a speech-driven web browser, in which commands are spoken into a microphone. These are examples of **adaptive technology** or **assistive technology**, and the design of a website can considerably help or hinder their use. For example, many web pages have a panel on the left or at the top with links to other parts of the site. The sighted user can easily ignore these if they are of no interest. Screen readers, however, often begin by reading out these links. This can be useful on the first

visit to a site, but on subsequent visits it can be frustrating for the user to have to endure the same recitation of links. A 'skip navigation' link or button right at the start of the page allows the user of a screen reader to skip this part of the page. In an accessible design, this 'skip navigation' facility can be invisible to a sighted user, but so placed that it is the first thing read by a screen reader.

For people who use a keyboard rather than a mouse, navigation is made easier if there are **access keys**. These are more-or-less standard keyboard shortcuts that can be incorporated into web pages. For instance, Alt 1 generally jumps to the homepage, Alt 4 jumps to a search facility. Alt 2 is generally a 'skip navigation' link, taking the user straight to the main content of a page.

access keys

Activity 29 (exploratory)

There are some optional accessibility features built into Windows, and you should spend a few minutes investigating them. If you go to the Control Panel (reached from the Start button, and possibly then via 'Settings'), you should see an icon labelled 'Accessibility Options'. These give you options relating mainly to your mouse and keyboard. If there is an option 'Configure Windows to work for your vision, hearing and mobility needs', note this will launch a 'wizard' that allows you to change your settings. If you are concerned that you might not be able to undo any changes, be sure not to select any modifications that are offered.

Depending on your version of Windows, you may find further accessibility tools if you go to the Windows Start button, choose 'Programs', select 'Accessories', and then select 'Accessibility'.

Comment

When I looked at these I was struck that the options available were quite modest: changes in text size in menus and dialogue boxes, the option to drive the cursor using the keypad rather than a mouse, and so on. I was interested to see that 'sticky keys' allows keys that sometimes have to be pressed simultaneously with other keys (mainly shift-, control- and alt-) to be pressed in sequence. I was very surprised that no single action can be used as a substitute for double-clicking.

Figures 12 and 13 show an example of an accessibility tool, developed in New Zealand. The Lomak ('light operated Mouse and Keyboard') replaces a standard computer keyboard and mouse. The user directs a light source at the keyboard to get standard keyboard and mouse functions. The light source can be worn on the head or be hand-held.

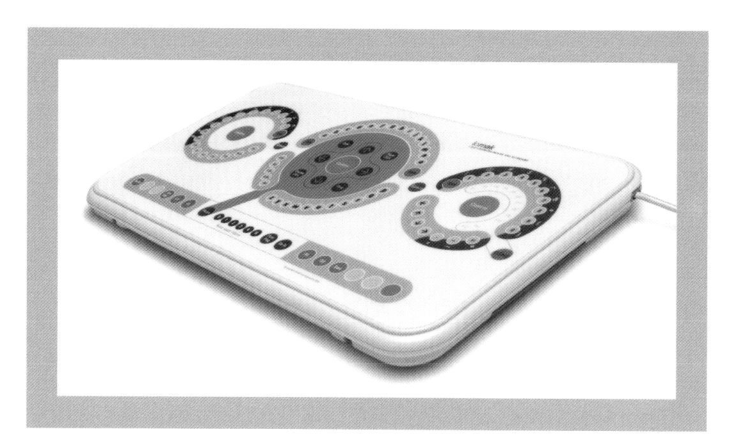

Figure 12 The Lomak keyboard. Standard keyboard and mouse functions are obtained by directing a light source at the keyboard

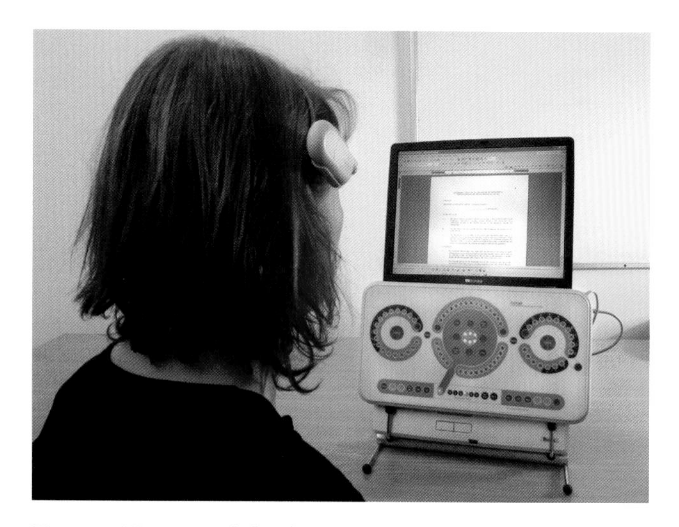

Figure 13 Lomak keyboard in use. The user is wearing the light source on her head, and directing it with head movements

Further information on accessibility aids can be found by searching the Web with terms such as 'adaptive technology', 'accessibility aids' and 'accessibility software'.

6 E-government: other views

As you come to the end of this block, I would like to offer some alternative views of what e-government could or should be. What these views have in common is the notion that ICTs have the power to transform radically the way things are done.

We saw at the start of this part of Block 4 that in the UK the e-government project grew out of ideas about modernising government. This is true of many other countries' e-government projects also. What 'modernisation' means is not entirely clear, although it presumably involves managerial and organisational changes as well as the use of ICTs. But, whatever it involves, for many critics of e-government there is a feeling that the institutions of government will remain in control of the way ICTs are used by government.

There are other views of what e-government should be like. Implicit in many of these views is the idea that democratic e-government is not just about government services being put online. Instead, there is a view that democracy involves critical scrutiny of government. From this point of view, ICTs are seen to offer new tools for this critical scrutiny, and new ways of interacting with government. ICTs therefore open the way for a different kind of e-government. The following extract, from the *Guardian* newspaper, gives a flavour of this other view:

> Tom Steinberg, director of mySociety and a former adviser to No 10, wants the project to show off the success of the people he calls 'civic coders'. Their grassroots projects typically run queries on data already published by the state, returning relevant information which is fed onto elegant, minimalist websites. Simple social software tools – email, blogs, message boards, wikis – add the crucial layer of interactivity, and in one swift hack, citizen is brought closer to state.
>
> FaxYourMP is the canonical example. Stefan Magdalinski, one of the site's volunteers, says the site came about because, 'we don't see why people should have to jump through hoops to contact their elected MP'. The site runs a postcode query to establish who your MP is, then presents you with a simple email form that quickly becomes a fax appearing in the MP's office. Run completely by volunteers, the site won the 2004 Future UK Internet Hero award and recently sent its 100,000th fax.

mySociety is an umbrella organisation of 'grassroots' e-government projects. No. 10 refers to 10 Downing Street, the official home of the British Prime Minister.

> FaxYourMP and the websites that followed it picked up tricks the government had missed. The sites have seen ways to recycle data the government already publishes, increasing the usefulness of that data, without incurring much further cost.
>
> Hogge (2004)

These 'grassroots' e-government organisations often criticise governments for not presenting information in a useful way:

> One thing he [Stefan Magdalinski, responsible for www.theyworkforyou.com] himself wants is for the Government to get out of the business of creating portals that the public is supposed to use as a gateway – [...]. 'They should get good at search-engine optimisation and which service-delivery points they want to optimise. If they want serious uptake, promote the places where you can actually pay your road tax above all the other areas.'
>
> More than that, says Magdalinski, they need to do a lot more to make data feeds available in formats that third parties can use. His own website is a case in point. 'The e-government framework has been going on for some years, but they still publish everything in PDF.' PDF, Adobe's portable document format that preserves formatting and can be read on almost any computing device, is good for forms and material that is going to be printed. But why produce the recent listing of MPs' expenses in that way, which makes it impossible to search them and to sort them meaningfully?
>
> For the kinds of services Magdalinski builds, PDF is a hindrance. He wants data published in standard machine-readable formats designed to allow re-use by third parties. By the next general election, theyworkforyou.com should be able to provide a detailed scorecard on every MP: voting record, speeches made in Parliament, expenses claims. And why shouldn't charities like the Royal National Institute for the Blind be able to scrape all relevant government information – legislation, direct links to benefits – into a website that is designed to make life easier for its members?
>
> Grossman (2004)

Data feeds are services that supply automatically updated information on a particular topic. The user generally needs special software. In this article, though, 'data feed' seems to mean just 'data'.

You can perhaps see here the emergence of a different view of the role of ICT in relation to government. In the 'conventional' view, ICT does not fundamentally change the relationship between government and the public, but allows government to do more efficiently and cheaply the kind of thing that it has always done, such as supplying information, collecting taxes, and so on. In the other, more subversive view, ICT has the potential to change the relationship between government and public, and to lead to different kinds of democratic process.

It seems particularly appropriate to end this block, by thinking about ICT's capacity for transformation. Like many new technologies, ICTs at first offer quicker or cheaper or more efficient ways of doing what is already done in other ways. But the cheapness, speed and accessibility of these technologies have a way of encouraging novel applications, by new groups of users – as demonstrated by the grassroots organisations mentioned in this section. ICTs can thus transform the world in ways that could not have been predicted at the outset. The early proponents of e-government would almost certainly not have viewed e-activism as part of their agenda.

Answers to self-assessment activities

Activity 1

The author–date citation is like this:

(Castells, 2000) or Castells (2000) if the author's name is part of a sentence.

The reference is like this:

Castells, M. (2000) *The Rise of the Network Society*, Oxford, Blackwell, p. 35.

Not all publishers include a place of publication in book references. Sometimes the order of publisher and place is reversed.

This book is actually the second edition of a book first published in 1996, as you may have spotted if you checked it in a library catalogue. The edition number is incorporated as follows.

Castells, M. (2000) *The Rise of the Network Society*, 2nd ed., Oxford, Blackwell, p. 35.

Activity 4

2% of 160 million calls is:

$$\frac{2}{100} \times 160\,000\,000 = 3\,200\,000$$

At £2.40 per call, this number of saved calls amounts to a saving of:

$$3\ 200\ 000 \times £2.40 = £7\ 680\ 000$$

As the data on which this calculation is based is only approximate, it is misleading to give such a precise answer. It would be better to round the answer to £8 million.

There would, of course, be the cost of setting up and maintaining the website to set against this, but the setting-up cost should be a 'one-off cost' rather than a recurring cost to pay each year. The maintenance cost would be an annual cost, but should be well below £8 million.

Activity 8

(a) If the course is never repeated, then we can safely use the course code as a key, because the code identifies something unique.

(b) If courses are repeated annually there is a problem with using the course code as a key because it no longer represents something unique. For instance, students enrolling for Yoga in successive years are enrolling for different instances of the course. Each instance of the course would need its own record in the database. However, if the database is made afresh each year, and just covers one year's

worth of data, then the problem does not arise and the course code can be used as a key.

(c) If courses are run twice or more per year, there is a problem with using the course code as a key for the same reasons as in (b). That is, each presentation of the course is a new instance (assuming the database has a lifetime of a year or more), and so the code does not represent something unique.

Activity 9

One entity is 'Committee'. The associated attribute is 'Meeting time'.

Another entity is 'Member'. The associated attribute is 'Telephone number'.

Activity 11

(a) A joining table is required because the relationship between 'Committee' and 'Member' is many-to-many. (A committee has several members, and each member can be on more than one committee.)

(b) See Table 8.

Table 8 Joining table for Activity 11

Committee	Member
Planning	Jones
Planning	Patel
Planning	Robinson
Recreation	Jones
Recreation	Smith
Education	Patel
Education	Robinson
Education	Smith

Activity 13

(a) Flat databases and relational databases.

(b) An entity is a distinct thing for which we wish to store information.

(c) A joining table is a means of relating entities by relating the records of each table through their keys.

Activity 18

(a) False match. Relaxing the matching criterion means making the matching process more tolerant of difference. This increases the likelihood that biometric data from different people will be judged to be from the same person.

(b) False non-match. Making the matching criterion stricter means that the comparison is less tolerant of difference. This means that we are more likely to decide that samples of data from the same person are from different people.

Activity 19

Compared to the false match rate of 1 in 100, the group size of 1 000 000 qualifies as large, so we can use the approximate method described above. To find the answer we need to divide 1 000 000 by 100. This gives 10 000. This is *approximately* the number of false matches we can expect.

Activity 21

(a) False negative identification error enables someone to re-enrol in the system under a new identity, and thereby get a second identity card. This possibly enables fraudulent use of services and is a security problem. False positive identification means (in this context) that an applicant is wrongly thought to have already enrolled. A new identity document will not be issued until the applicant can prove his or her true identity by other means. False positive identification is not a security risk because no new documents are issued until the confusion is resolved.

(b) False positive identification creates extra work for the operators of the system sorting out the misidentification. Therefore a usable system should have a low probability of false positive identification.

Activity 22

Iris scans from a single eye, or fingerprints from a few fingers, do not give a sufficiently low false match rate. Using both eyes, or more fingers, improves the false match rate to a suitable value for a practical system.

Activity 23

The problems Dettmer mentions nearly all relate to setting up a national database for an identification system. For instance, he mentions uncertainty over 'how long it will take to enrol users in a real system' and 'what percentage of the population will be unable to travel to their local biometric registration centre'. He says very little about the use of the card for verification.

Activity 24

(a) This can be resolved experimentally, so looks like a technical matter.

(b) It is hard to answer this without asking further questions about what the information will be used for and why. These look like ethical, social and political questions.

(c) This looks like a technical matter. However, if differential pricing is used, deciding how much different categories of people should be charged takes on ethical, political and social aspects.

(d) This looks as though it could be settled by experiment, so it looks like a technical matter.

(e) This does not look as though it could be resolved with a purely factual input, so it has ethical, political and social aspects.

(f) Again, these do not look as though they could be resolved with a purely factual input, so ethical, political and social issues are raised.

Activity 26

Text (b) is much more scannable (to use Nielsen's term) than (a). It is easier to take in text (b) at a glance than text (a). This is because the paragraphs are shorter, the sentences are shorter (and simpler), and important sequences of ideas are listed ('collated' and 'optimised for the Web').

References

Bisson, S. (2005) 'Mark of success', *Guardian* 'Life' supplement, 10 February, p. 16.

Bly, S. (1997) 'Field work: Is it Product Work?', *ACM Interactions Magazine*, January and February, pp. 25–30; quoted in Preece et al. (2002), p. 387.

Bowcott, O. (2004) 'Top security jails install fingerprint scan at gates', *Guardian*, 5 August, 2004.

Cabinet Office (1999) *Modernising Government*, London, Cabinet Office.

Cabinet Office (2000) *e-Government: a Strategic Framework for Public Services in the Information Age*, London, Cabinet Office.

Cabinet Office (2003) *Quality Framework for UK Government Website Design: Usability Issues for Government Websites*, London, Cabinet Office.

The Cabinet Office documents are available online and can be downloaded as PDF documents from http://www.cabinetoffice.gov.uk/publications/. Use the search facility to find a document by title.

Cross, M. (2005) 'Local solution to the Identity Crisis', *Guardian*, Online supplement, 31 March 2005, p. 16.

Dempsey, P. (2005) 'Knowing me, knowing you', *IEE Information Professional*, Institution of Electrical Engineers, February/March 2005, pp. 14–18.

Dettmer, R. (2004) 'Safety in Numbers', *IEE Review*, vol. 50, no.11, November, pp. 28–9.

The Economist (2005) 'New Look Passports', 19 February, p. 83.

Grossman, W. (2004) 'Are We E-fficient?', *The Independent*, Science & Technology, 24 November, p. 11.

Hogge, B. (2004) 'Closer to the state', *Guardian* Online supplement, 2 December, p. 19.

Mansfield, A. and Rejman-Greene, M., (2003) *Feasibility Study on the Use of Biometrics in An Entitlement Scheme*, National Physical Laboratory, Teddington, version 3. Available online at http://www.npl.co.uk/scientific_software/research/biometrics/

Musgrave, S. (2005) 'Community portals – the UK experience', *Journal of Community Informatics*, vol. 1, no. 2, p. 35.

Nielsen, J. (1997) 'How users read on the Web' [online] http://www.useit.com/alertbox/9710a.html [Accessed 21 November 2005].

Nielsen, J. (1998) 'Top Ten Mistakes in Web Design' [online] http://www.useit.com/alertbox/9605.html [Accessed 21 November 2005].

Preece, J., Rogers, Y. and Sharp, H. (2002), *Interaction Design*, Hoboken, Wiley & Sons, p. 27.

Say, M. (2005) 'The Information Man', *Government Computing*, Vol. 19, No. 2, February 2005, p. 16.

Silcock, R. (2001) 'What is e-government?', *Parliamentary Affairs*, Vol. 54, No. 1, January, p. 97.

ACKNOWLEDGEMENTS

Grateful acknowledgement is made to the following sources for permission to reproduce material within this book.

Text

Roger Dettmer, 'Safety in Numbers,' *IEE Review*, vol. 50, no. 11, Nov 2004.

Hogge B., (2004), 'Closer to the State'. The *Guardian* Newspaper issued 2nd December 2004.

Figures

Figure 12: By permission of Lomak International

Figure 13: By permission of Lomak International